INORGANIC ION EXCHANGERS

TOPICS IN INORGANIC
AND GENERAL CHEMISTRY

A COLLECTION OF MONOGRAPHS EDITED BY

P. L. ROBINSON

Emeritus Professor of Chemistry in the University of Durham and the University of Newcastle upon Tyne

MONOGRAPH 2

INORGANIC
ION EXCHANGERS

BY

C. B. AMPHLETT, Ph. D., D. Sc.

Chemistry Division,
Atomic Energy Research Establishment,
Harwell, Berks. (Great Britain)

ELSEVIER PUBLISHING COMPANY

AMSTERDAM/LONDON/NEW YORK

1964

ELSEVIER PUBLISHING COMPANY
335 JAN VAN GALENSTRAAT, P. O. BOX 211, AMSTERDAM

AMERICAN ELSEVIER PUBLISHING COMPANY, INC.
52 VANDERBILT AVENUE, NEW YORK, N.Y. 10017

ELSEVIER PUBLISHING COMPANY LIMITED
12B, RIPPLESIDE COMMERCIAL ESTATE
RIPPLE ROAD, BARKING, ESSEX

LIBRARY OF CONGRESS CATALOG CARD NUMBER 64-14177

WITH 36 ILLUSTRATIONS AND 32 TABLES

To my Wife

Preface

The study of inorganic ion exchangers has in the past been overshadowed by the much greater interest in organic ion-exchange resins, while the industrial applications of ion exchange have relied heavily on the latter materials. It is thus interesting to discover that the first systematic studies on ion exchange were carried out on naturally-occurring inorganic materials, *viz.* the clay fractions of the soil, which were investigated as long ago as 1850; furthermore, the first industrial applications of synthetic ion exchangers for water-softening also employed inorganic materials in the early years of this century. The subsequent development of organic exchangers possessing greater stability, and capable of controlled synthesis to give products with reproducible properties, has largely displaced their inorganic counterparts in modern technology.

The revived interest in inorganic exchangers stems largely from the fact that they are more stable than the organic resins under certain conditions, *e.g.* high temperatures or the presence of ionizing radiation. New types have been developed possessing greater stability than the early aluminosilicate exchangers, and which are in some cases highly selective towards certain ions. Apart from considerations of possible applications, the study of many inorganic ion exchangers is of interest in itself for the light which it throws upon problems such as the sorption of ions by precipitates, the electrophoretic behaviour of suspensions, the diffusion of ions in crystals, isotopic exchange in heterogeneous systems, and many examples in the field of structural chemistry. Furthermore, in many rigid three-dimensional exchangers, where swelling is not possible, the theoretical treatment of the thermodynamics and kinetics of exchange is frequently much simpler than in the organic resins, although steric effects and the limited miscibility of solid phases may sometimes lead to complications.

The present monograph is not exhaustive, but serves as a guide to the present state of the subject. A brief introductory chapter deals with some general questions of ion-exchange behaviour and considers a number of miscellaneous inorganic exchangers which to date have received little attention; the principal classes of inorganic exchanger are then treated in turn, emphasising wherever possible the similarities and differences which exist between them.

Inorganic exchangers, particularly those of the zirconium phosphate and zirconium oxide types, are today undergoing a rapid development which in some respects resembles that of the organic resins thirty years ago, although as yet no industrial applications are in sight. There is little doubt, however, that in due course they will take their place alongside the others, not as competitors, but as allies, each type fulfilling the functions to which it is best suited.

Acknowledgements

I am indebted to various journals for permission to reproduce figures from publications contained in them, and to Professor P. L. Robinson for constant advice and encouragement.

Harwell, March 1964   C. B. AMPHLETT

Contents

Glossary of Terms

The symbols used throughout this book are given below; owing to variations in usage between different authors they may sometimes differ from those in the original references. Definitions are given in the text where appropriate.

K_d Distribution coefficient (p. 2); $K_d{}^A$ refers to the species A.

$K_A{}^B$ Selectivity quotient (p. 2) for an exchanger relative to species B and A.

K' Mass action constant (p. 25) corrected for solution activities

$$\left(= \frac{\gamma_A}{\gamma_B} \cdot K_A{}^B \right)$$

K Thermodynamic equilibrium constant (p. 24).

α Separation factor for two ions on an exchanger; theoretically, for two species A and B, $\alpha_A{}^B = K_d{}^B / K_d{}^A$.

[ ]   Concentration of species, usually in milliequivalents (meq) per ml of solution or per gram of solid.

{ }   Activity of species.

q_A Uptake of species A by exchanger at equilibrium, in meq/g.

q_o Saturation capacity of exchanger in meq/g.

N_A Mole fraction of ion A in exchanger $= q_A/q_o$.

γ_A Activity coefficient of A in solution.

Γ_A Activity coefficient of A in exchanger.

c_A Concentration of A in solution at equilibrium, in meq/ml.

c_o Total solution concentration in meq/ml.

D^i Ionic diffusion coefficient in the solid phase (p. 66).

CHAPTER 1

Introduction

In ion-exchange reactions a reversible interchange of ions takes place between two compounds, one of which (the ion exchanger) is insoluble in the medium in which the exchange is carried out. As an example, we may consider a cation-exchange resin such as Dowex–50, which consists of a highly cross-linked sulphonated polystyrene polymer network. If free sulphonic acid groups are present the resin is said to be in the hydrogen form, and when immersed in an aqueous medium it behaves as a strong acid; the sulphonic acid groups are completely dissociated, the acidity of the aqueous medium within the resin structure being approximately 5 N. On treatment with alkali the acid is neutralized and the exchanger converted to the appropriate cationic form. Partial conversion also occurs when the resin is immersed in the appropriate salt solution, since cations are able to flow freely into and out of the polymer network provided that electroneutrality is preserved. In the latter case, since the exchange is an equilibrium process, complete conversion is only possible if a considerable excess of the exchanging cation is used, or if the ions released from the resin are continuously removed from the solution, $e.g.$ by employing a flow technique rather than batch equilibration. A similar exchange of cations will take place between a resin in one cationic form and another cation in solution, and the process may be represented by the following equation, where M^- represents the polymer network and A^+ and B^+ are both cations:

$$M^-A^+ + B^+ \rightleftharpoons M^-B^+ + A^+ \tag{1}$$

The anion present in solution does not partake in the exchange to an appreciable extent, since consideration of the Donnan equilibrium and the insolubility of the exchanger anion M^- (the gegenion) shows that the anion in solution cannot enter the network. The above equilibrium obeys the law of mass action, and a thermodynamic equilibrium constant may be derived for the exchange. Two practical quantities which represent the extent to which exchange takes place are the distribution coefficient K_d and the selectivity quotient $K_A{}^B$, both of which are experimentally-determined quantities; calculation of the equilibrium constant for other than ideal systems requires a knowledge of the activity coefficients of the exchanging ions in the solid phase and in solution (p. 24). The distribution coefficient is defined as the number of milliequivalents of an ion absorbed per gram of exchanger divided by the number of milliequivalents of that ion per ml remaining in solution at equilibrium, and is therefore a direct measure of the extent to which an ion is removed from solution when the exchanger is added. The selectivity quotient, on the other hand, refers to both the ions concerned in the exchange and is equal to the ratio of the concentrations of the two ions in the solid phase divided by that of their concentrations in solution, again at equilibrium; it is thus a direct measure of the preference of the exchanger for one ion relative to the other, and is sometimes termed the stoichiometric equilibrium ratio, since for the equilibrium (1) above it is given by the expression

$$K_A{}^B = \frac{[\overline{B^+}]\,[A^+]}{[B^+]\,[\overline{A^+}]} \tag{2}$$

where the barred quantities represent concentrations in the solid phase and the others concentrations in solution. $K_A{}^B$ and K_d may be related to each other if we know the saturation capacity of the exchanger q_0 (the total number of milliequivalents of exchangeable cations per gram) and the concentration of the initial solution c_0 milliequivalents per ml, since $[A^+] + [B^+] = c_0$ and $[\overline{A^+}] + [\overline{B^+}] = q_0$. Thus, if we take an exchanger containing only A^+ cations, capacity q_0 meq/g, and immerse it in a solution containing B^+ cations only, concentration c_0 meq/ml, and if the equilibrium concentrations are [A$^+$] and [B$^+$] in solution and [$\overline{A^+}$] and [$\overline{B^+}$] on the exchanger, we have the following relationships:

$$K_d{}^B = \frac{[\overline{B^+}]}{[B^+]}$$

$$K_A{}^B = \frac{[\overline{B^+}]\,[A^+]}{[B^+]\,[\overline{A^+}]} = \frac{[\overline{B^+}]\,(c_0 - [B^+])}{[B^+]\,(q_0 - [\overline{B^+}])} = K_d{}^B.\frac{c_0 - [B^+]}{q_0 - [\overline{B^+}]}$$

If we now consider absorption of B$^+$ from a solution in which it is a tracer component, *i.e.* [B$^+$] $\ll c_0$ and [$\overline{B^+}$] $\ll q_0$, the above expression may be written approximately as

$$K_A{}^B \approx K_d{}^B \frac{c_0}{q_0} \tag{3}$$

and values of $K_A{}^B$ may be obtained from measurements of distribution coefficients under these conditions. From the same expression we see that

$$K_d{}^B \approx K_A{}^B \frac{q_0}{c_0} \tag{4}$$

i.e. the distribution coefficient is inversely proportional to the concentration of the solution. If in a solution containing both A$^+$ and B$^+$ ions we consider the total concentration to be approximately equal to the concentration [A$^+$] when B$^+$ is the tracer component, then $K_d{}^B$ is proportional to [A$^+$]$^{-1}$, or in the more general case of the exchange between B^{n+} and A$^+$ to [A$^+$]$^{-n}$; in the general case, if the law of mass action is obeyed, a plot of log $K_d{}^B$ *versus* log [A$^+$] will be a straight line of slope $-n$, thus enabling the charge on the exchanging ion to be derived.

The sulphonic acid resins have as their anion-exchanging counterparts strongly basic resins in which the functional groups on the polymer network are positively-charged quaternary ammonium groups, the exchanging ions being OH$^-$ or other anions. Weakly basic and weakly acidic exchangers also exist, in which the ionization is negligible except in acidic and basic solutions respectively.

References p. 14

Weakly basic anion exchangers contain tertiary amine groups, while weakly acidic cation exchangers usually contain either carboxylic groups (which ionize at pH $\geqslant$ 7) or phenolic groups (which do not ionize appreciably below pH 12). Bifunctional cation exchangers such as phenolsulphonic acid resins have two types of exchanging group, one strongly acidic and the other not exchanging until the solution is quite alkaline. Further references to the organic ion-exchange resins will be found in standard texts[1].

HISTORICAL DEVELOPMENT OF ION-EXCHANGE MATERIALS

The earliest systematic studies in which ion-exchange properties were described are concerned with base exchange in minerals present in the soil[2]. Before the existence of ions in solution was demonstrated, and before the crystal structure of the solid concerned had been elucidated, it was found that when soils are treated with solutions of ammonium salts ammonia is taken up by the soil and an equivalent quantity of calcium released. This property of "base exchange" was shown to be reversible and to involve chemically equivalent quantities of the base taken up and of that released; moreover, it was shown to hold for a number of other salts besides those of ammonia. Although many years were to elapse before the mechanism was understood—since this demands a knowledge both of the ionic nature of the solutions and of the crystal structure and composition of the clay minerals present in the soil—it was recognized as a phenomenon of considerable importance in relation to soil fertility. Some soils possess the property to a greater extent than others, and these are generally more fertile, and more capable of storing mineral fertilisers over a long period when these are applied to the soil.

Many hypotheses have been proposed to explain the phenomenon of base exchange in soils[3], but ultimately it was traced to two principal causes. One of these is the presence of humins and humic acids, particularly in soils rich in organic matter, where the decay of the latter produces a wide variety of ill-defined organic species which possess hydroxyl or carboxyl groups which can act as ion-exchange groups in the same way as in the phenolic and carboxylic acid resins. However, in many soils of low organic content, and in soils where organic matter has been destroyed by treatment with hydrogen peroxide, a considerable ion-exchange capacity is still observed; on fractionation of the soil by removal of coarse mineral matter and careful elutriation this may be traced to the so-called "colloid fraction", which on petrographic and X-ray examination is found to consist chiefly of clay minerals. A close identification of the ion-exchange properties of soils with their clay fraction has been achieved, the gross properties of the soil depending upon the amount and types of clay minerals present (p. 24). Other alumino-silicates may confer ion-exchange properties in certain soils, e.g. glauconite, a ferrous aluminosilicate analogous to the zeolites, which possesses exchangeable potassium; this mineral exchanges only at the crystal surfaces, but in colloidal form possesses considerable capacity.

The first synthetic ion exchangers were also inorganic materials; these were the synthetic zeolites or permutites developed by Gans and other workers for use in water-softening processes[4]. They are synthetic sodium aluminosilicates in which sodium is replaced by calcium when hard water is percolated through a bed of the material; since the reaction is reversible the exchanger may be regenerated by treatment with a saturated brine solution when exhausted. Two principal types of permutites may be distinguished, viz. the fusion permutites and the gel permutites. The former are prepared by fusing together mixtures of soda, potash, felspar and kaolin, and are generally similar to the natural zeolites (chapter 3) except that they have a more irregular structure. The gel permutites may be prepared by a method which allows more careful control of the reaction conditions and of the properties and composition of the product. Alkali is added in controlled proportions to acid solutions of aluminium sulphate and sodium silicate to produce a gelatinous precipitate; this on drying produces irregular particles of a gel which resembles silica gel in appearance.

A third method which has been used extensively for studies on synthetic crystalline zeolites involves slow hydrothermal crystallization at elevated temperatures from solutions of silica, alumina and alkali. As an example we may consider the preparation of synthetic aluminosilicates having the general formula $Na_2O \cdot Al_2O_3 \cdot nSiO_2$, when $n = 1$–12. Commercial sodium aluminate ("Alfloc") is dissolved in water and the ferric hydroxide filtered off, after which the appropriate quantity of an alkaline silica sol is added (e.g. Syton X, a preparation containing 30 wt.% SiO_2 at pH $\sim$ 10); since silica gels in the presence of sodium ions, the solutions must be stirred well. AnalaR sodium hydroxide is then added to give the required excess of sodium above a ratio of Na: Al = 1:1 and the solution is heated in sealed Pyrex tubes between 60–110°C or at higher temperatures in stainless steel autoclaves. Mixed sodium–potassium forms can be prepared using potassium hydroxide solutions of aluminium oxide and adding sodium hydroxide before the final crystallization.

Gallium and germanium analogues have been prepared by similar methods, e.g. sodium gallosilicate, gallogermanate and aluminogermanate[5]. Ga_2O_3 or GeO_2 is dissolved in aqueous NaOH, filtered and acidified with hydrochloric acid, after which $Ga(OH)_3$ or H_2GeO_3 is precipitated by adding ammonia. Alkaline solutions or dispersions of the precipitate (0.5 M $NaGaO_2$ or Na_2GeO_3) are then mixed with the appropriate partners (gallate + silica sol, gallate + germanate, aluminate + germanate) and the preparations are completed as in the case of the aluminosilicates.

Following the earlier development of the crude synthetic zeolites for water-softening applications, the subsequent development of organic ion exchangers later in this century displaced the former both in scientific studies and in practical applications. The first organic exchangers were poorly-defined materials prepared by suitable treatment (oxidation, sulphonation, etc.) of natural products such as coal and wood, but the later synthesis of condensation resins and later still that of emulsion polymers based on polystyrene enabled spherical beads to be produced in which close control is possible of particle size, chemical composition and ion-exchange properties. Moreover, modern ion exchange resins exchange much more rapidly than the zeolites and can be converted into acid forms by treatment with acids, whereas the aluminosilicates are unstable in acid solution. During the period from 1925 onwards there developed a rapidly-expanding study of the organic ion-exchange resins, with considerable emphasis on practical applications[6]; in contrast, the study of inorganic exchangers was undertaken almost solely in relation to problems of structural chemistry and diffusion in solid systems.

Just as the applications of the zeolites are limited by their instability in acid solutions, so are those of organic resins limited by breakdown in aqueous systems at high temperatures and in presence of ionizing radiation; for these reasons there has been a resurgence of interest in inorganic exchangers in recent years, since they are particularly stable under these conditions. Applications which have been suggested include the ion-exchange absorption and fixation of highly active waste solutions on clays[7], and the use of other inorganic exchangers for water treatment at high temperatures and for chemical processing of highly-active solutions. This has led to considerable interest in the fundamental studies of these systems, which are described in the chapters which follow.

BASIC TYPES OF INORGANIC ION-EXCHANGE MATERIALS

(A) *Exchangers possessing well-defined crystal structures*	(i) *Aluminosilicates*
	(a) Two-dimensional layer-lattice structures, *e.g.* the clays and lamellar zeolites
	(b) Three-dimensional cage structures, *e.g.* the typical zeolites
	(ii) *Non-siliceous materials, e.g.* heteropolyacid salts
(B) *Poorly crystalline and amorphous materials*	(i) Hydrous oxides of polyvalent metals
	(ii) Acid salts of polyvalent metals and polybasic acids

The wide variety of inorganic exchangers may conveniently be

References p. 14

divided into a small number of basic types. Some of these materials are described in detail in the following chapters; others, of which less is known, are described briefly below. The principal types are shown in the scheme on page 7.

MISCELLANEOUS EXCHANGERS

In addition to the principal types of inorganic exchanger there are several interesting examples which have so far received little attention (Table 1), many of them being chemically complex but possessing well-defined crystal structures; only two of these are anion exchangers, *viz.* apatite and mercarbide.

Apatite is a naturally-occurring phosphatic mineral consisting of basic calcium phosphate; the fluorine analogue in which fluorine replaces the hydroxyl group is also known and occurs naturally as fluorapatite. The hydroxyl group in apatite is also replaced by fluoride when apatite is treated with solutions containing fluoride

TABLE 1

SOME MISCELLANEOUS INORGANIC ION EXCHANGERS

[R. M. Barrer, *Chem. Ind. (London)*, (1962) 1258]

Exchanger	Ideal formula	Capacity meq/g
Potassium polyphosphate	$K[PO_3]$	8.50
Sodium trititanate	$Na_2[Ti_3O_7]$	6.62
Sodium mercuriamidosul- phonate	$Na[HgNSO_3]$	3.30
Uranium micas	$H_3O[UO_2PO_4] \cdot xH_2O$	2.60 (anhydrous)
	$H_3O[UO_2AsO_4] \cdot xH_2O$	2.33 (anhydrous)
	$H_3O[UO_2VO_4] \cdot xH_2O$	2.48 (anhydrous)
Magnesium hexamethyl- enetetramine hexa- cyanoferrate(III)	$Mg[Mg((CH_2)_6N_4)_2Fe(CN)_6]_2 \cdot 24H_2O$	1.74
Graphite oxide	$C_7O_4H_2$	0.7–1.5
Mercarbide salts	$[C_2Hg_6O_2]Cl_2 \cdot 2H_2O$	1.5 (anhydrous)
	$[C_2Hg_6O_2]Br_2$	1.41 (anhydrous)
	$[C_2Hg_6O_2](OH)_2$	1.50 (anhydrous)

Square brackets enclose the basic units of the structural frameworks.

ion, the exchange being reversible. Cation exchange is also possible in hydroxyapatites, and since the latter form the basic compound in bone and teeth structures the process is important physiologically.

Selective uptake is observed among the alkali metals, sodium being absorbed preferentially compared with potassium[8]. Results obtained with a series of apatitic calcium phosphates of varying basicity[9] indicate that the general formula is

$$Ca_{10-x}H_x(PO_4)_6(OH)_{2-x}$$

with $0 < x \leqslant 2$, the common member of the series corresponding to $x = 0$, with a $PO_4:Ca$ ratio of 1.67 similar to that in many preparations of zirconium phosphate (p. 94). Although some exchange with hydrogen might be expected as well as with calcium, this has not been observed, indicating either that the affinity for hydrogen ion is extremely high or that hydrogen is covalently bound within the structure.

Apatite has been suggested[10] for the treatment of radioactive waste solutions containing ^{90}Sr, and it has been shown that a column containing 50 g of the crushed mineral (particle size 0.25–1.0 mm) will remove $> 99\%$ of the strontium from a feed solution containing $3\ M$ $NaNO_3$ and 2 mg $Sr(NO_3)_2$/ml for 27 column volumes at a linear flow-rate of 7 cm/h.

Mercarbide, or more correctly mercarbide salts, are prepared[11] by heating together mercury, potassium hydroxide and absolute alcohol at the boiling point. Final treatment of the product with nitric acid gives a product having the approximate composition $(CHg_3O)_n^{n+} (NO_3^-)_n$, in which nitrate ion may be replaced by other anions, the affinity increasing in the order

$$NO_3^- < Cl^- < Br^- < OH^- \lesssim CN^- < I^-.$$

Although the structure is not known, it is likely to contain polymeric chains.

Cation exchange is observed in many condensed *polyphosphates* such as sodium polyphosphate[12]. Conductivity titrations *versus* calcium, barium and lanthanum acetates and *versus* thorium tetrachloride have been interpreted in terms of replacement of the monovalent cation in the polyphosphate by the polyvalent cation[13]. The *mercuriamidosulphonate salts* also form long-chain structures in which replacement of the cation is possible[12]. The insoluble anion in these compounds has the structure shown below. Both the poly-

$$
\begin{array}{c}
SO_3^- \\
| \\
N \\
\diagup \quad \diagdown \\
Hg \qquad Hg \\
\diagup \qquad\qquad \diagdown \\
N \qquad\qquad N \\
| \qquad\qquad | \\
SO_3^- \qquad SO_3^-
\end{array}
$$

phosphates and the mercuriamidosulphonates swell freely in organic liquids, particularly when hydrogen bonding between adjacent chains is absent. Thus the quaternary ammonium forms of both types of compound swell in two dimensions (along the chains and parallel to them), but in the primary and secondary alkylammonium polyphosphates (where hydrogen bonding is possible) swelling is limited and the material behaves as a layer structure in which the parallel chains are bound into sheets by hydrogen bonds.

Table 1 also includes a number of true layer compounds with structures and properties which resemble those of the clays (chapter 2). Graphite oxide[14] and the uranium micas[15] show similar swelling properties to the clays, and like the latter are able to absorb long-chain organic ions. The area of lamellar surface available per cation in the uranium micas, as calculated from structural data and the measured exchange capacity, is 25 Å^2 compared with 24 Å^2 for the micaceous clay minerals muscovite and biotite, while the cross-sectional area of a normal paraffin chain is $\sim$ 20 Å^2. In order to accommodate a monolayer of stearylammonium ions, $C_{17}H_{35}NH_3^+$, in the interlayer spaces it would be necessary for the chains to be vertically oriented (p. 39), and when the interlayer distance in the alkylammonium uranium micas is measured it is found that it increases regularly as the chain length of the substituting ion is increased (Table 2). The distance in the water-free NH_4^+ form is 6.3 Å, and the increase on replacing the cation by RNH_3^+ is given by the expression

TABLE 2

LAYER EXPANSION (Δ) IN ALKYLAMMONIUM URANIUM MICAS[15]

Alkyl group	Interlayer distance in dry exchange form	Δ relative to NH_4^+ form	Calculated Δ (*)
Propyl	13.2 Å	6.9 Å	6.0 Å
Butyl	14.2	7.9	7.3
Pentyl	15.3	9.0	8.5
Hexyl	16.6	10.3	9.8
Heptyl	18.2	11.9	11.0
Octyl	18.6	12.3	12.3
Dodecyl	23.5	17.2	17.4
Stearyl	28.0	21.7	24.9

* calculated from $\Delta = 1.26\,(n-1) + 3.54$, where n is the number of carbon atoms in the alkyl chain.

$$\Delta = [1.26\,(n-1) + 3.54]\ \text{Å}$$

where n is the number of carbon atoms in the chain and the contribution of the terminal methyl group is taken as 3.54 Å.

It is questionable whether graphite oxide should be regarded as an inorganic exchanger, since the exchanging groups are largely, if not entirely, carboxyl groups. It may be prepared[14] by oxidation of graphite with either $KClO_3$ in mixed sulphuric–nitric acids or with a sulphuric acid solution of $NaNO_3$ and $KMnO_4$. Samples prepared in this way possessed carbon : oxygen ratios varying from 2.53 to 2.83. Titration against alkali indicated that the concentration of titratable hydroxyl groups was $\sim$ 6–10 meq/g, while esterification with different reagents and exchange with calcium ions gave values ranging from 0.4 to 7 meq/g, suggesting that several different carboxylic acid groups of varying acidity may be present. Membranes have been prepared by evaporating a suspension of the material on a porous glass plate, and these have been used in concentration cells. Large cations pass readily through the membranes, but sodium and lithium ions cause swelling and destruction.

Another cation exchanger which has recently been reported[19] is prepared by mixing dilute solutions of sodium molybdate and potassium ferrocyanide in 0.5 N HCl; the precipitate is washed with dilute HCl and dried at 100 °C. Precipitates of this type have previously been stated to possess the composition $(MoO_2)_2Fe(CN)_6$ when the ratio of molybdenum to iron in the reactants is $2:1$, but when this ratio is increased the composition of the solid tends to a limiting value of $Mo:Fe = 2.8:1$; this suggests that polymerized and hydrolysed molybdenyl species such as

$$MoO_3H^+, \quad [MoO_2(MoO_3)_x]^{2+} \text{ and } [MoO_2H(MoO_3)_x]^+$$

may be present in the structure, with $x = 1, 2, 3$. The product is stable in dilute acid solutions and possesses interesting and possibly useful exchange properties, which presumably involve exchange of hydrogen ion in the hydrolysed forms. Tracer uptake measurements from $0.5 \ N \ HNO_3$ solutions show values of K_d of $2 \cdot 10^4$ for caesium, $6 \cdot 10^2$ for strontium and $8 \cdot 10^2$ for europium; the value for strontium is comparable to that for caesium on zirconium phosphate (p. 105) and suggests that a combination of the latter and molybdenyl ferrocyanide in series might be used to remove both caesium and strontium from highly-active fission product waste solutions, provided that the rare earths are sequestered before removing strontium. The tungsten analogue, which is more stable in acid solution, may prove to be even more useful.

ANALOGUES OF THE ALUMINOSILICATES: ISOMORPHOUS REPLACEMENT

Reference is made above (p. 6) to the preparation of gallium and germanium analogues of the zeolites in which gallium replaces aluminium and germanium replaces silicon. Selbin and Mason[16] have prepared the following analogues for comparison with the zeolites:

(*i*) $Na_2O \cdot Ga_2O_3 \cdot 2.8SiO_2$ and $Na_2O \cdot 1.27Ga_2O_3 \cdot 3.15SiO_2$, neither of which shows ion-exchange properties, although the second possesses a sodalite structure.

(*ii*) $Na_2O \cdot Ga_2O_3 \cdot 2.60SiO_2$, with a structure analogous to Linde Sieve 13X (p. 55), the X-ray patterns being almost identical. This possesses exchange properties.

(*iii*) Mixed gallium–aluminium sieves containing 7–20% wt.%

Ga_2O_3 and ratios of Al:Ga up to 1:1. These all give patterns similar to Sieve 13X and absorb *n*-heptane and toluene efficiently.

Another class of analogous materials is exemplified by the *gallocarbonates*, which posses the general formula

$$Na_2O \cdot Ga_2O_3 \cdot 2CO_2 \cdot nH_2O,$$

and are prepared by reacting together solutions of sodium gallate and sodium bicarbonate[17]; on stirring the product with silver nitrate solution at room temperature silver replaces sodium to give a product which analyses as $1.10Ag_2O \cdot Ga_2O_3 \cdot 1.92CO_2 \cdot 5.7H_2O$ and possesses a different X-ray pattern from that expected for a mixture of $Ga(OH)_3$ and Ag_2CO_3. Sodium aluminocarbonate may be similarly prepared and shows the same behaviour, but the compounds are slowly decomposed by water, even at room temperature, and are therefore of little practical utility.

The replacement reactions considered in this book are those which take place readily under not too drastic conditions, *e.g.* by treatment of the solid with aqueous solutions, usually at temperatures not exceeding 100 °C. These are the types of reaction to which the term ion exchange is usually applied. There are, however, more profound changes in which isomorphous replacement is possible, which may also be regarded as a form of ion exchange; these are frequently found among the aluminosilicates, but in order to carry them out it is necessary to crystallize the materials from melts of the appropriate composition, *e.g.* Si may be replaced reversibly[18] by KAl and by NaAl. The syntheses of the gallium and germanium analogues described above may be regarded as examples where replacement is structurally feasible but cannot be readily achieved by normal means. The distinction between this type of behaviour and true ion exchange is however an artificial one, since the mobility even of simple cations in inorganic exchangers can vary greatly, and in some cases is effectively zero (p. 50); similarly, there are cases in the clay minerals where ions which diffuse into the lattice can become fixed and resistant to further exchange (p. 19). It is however a field which has been little explored, and one which we might expect to be of considerable future interest.

REFERENCES

1 J. A. KITCHENER, *Ion-Exchange Resins*, Methuen, London, 1957; F. HELFFERICH, *Ion Exchange*, McGraw-Hill, New York, 1962.
2 H. S. THOMPSON, *J. Roy. Agr. Soc., Engl.*, 11 (1850) 68; J. F. WAY, *J. Roy. Agr. Soc., Engl.*, 11 (1850) 313; 13 (1852) 123.
3 W. P. KELLEY, *Ion Exchange in Soils*, Reinhold, New York, 1948.
4 R. GANS, *Jahrb. Preuss. Geol. Landesanstalt (Berlin)*, 26 (1905) 179; Ger. Patent 174, 097 (1906).
5 R. M. BARRER, J. W. BAYNHAM, F. W. BULTITUDE AND W. M. MEIER, *J. Chem. Soc.*, (1959) 195.
6 F. C. NACHOD AND J. SCHUBERT, *Ion-Exchange Technology*, Academic Press, New York, 1956.
7 L. P. HATCH, *Am. Scientist*, 41 (1953) 410.
8 W. R. STOLL AND W. F. NEUMAN, *J. Am. Chem. Soc.*, 78 (1956) 1585.
9 L. WINAND, M. J. DALLEMAGNE AND G. DUYCKAERTS, *Nature*, 190 (1961) 164.
10 L. L. AMES, J. R. McHENRY AND J. F. HONSTEAD, *Proc. Second Int. Conf. Peaceful Uses Atomic Energy*, United Nations, Geneva, 18 (1959) 76.
11 A. WEISS AND A. WEISS, *Z. Anorg. Allgem. Chem.*, 282 (1955) 324.
12 A. WEISS AND E. MICHEL, *Z. Anorg. Allgem. Chem.*, 296 (1958) 313; 306 (1960) 277; *Z. Naturforsch.*, 15b (1960) 679.
13 E. THILO, A. SONNTAG AND K. H. RATTAY, *Z. Anorg. Allgem. Chem.*, 283 (1956) 365.
14 H. P. BOEHM, A. CLAUSS AND U. HOFMANN, *J. Chim. Phys.*, 58 (1961) 141.
15 A. WEISS, K. HARTL AND U. HOFMANN, *Z. Naturforsch.*, 12b (1957) 351.
16 J. SELBIN AND R. B. MASON, *J. Inorg. Nucl. Chem.*, 20 (1961) 222.
17 T. V. PERMANOVA AND I. S. LILEEV, *Russian J. Inorg. Chem.*, 5 (1960) 479.
18 R. M. BARRER AND J. W. BAYNHAM, *J. Chem. Soc.*, (1956) 2892.
19 L. BAETSLÉ AND P. DEJONGHE, *Treatment and Storage of High-Level Radioactive Wastes*, International Atomic Energy Agency, Vienna, 1963, p. 553.

CHAPTER 2

The clay minerals

The clay minerals comprise a complex series of aluminosilicate structures in which a number of basic types shade almost imperceptibly into each other, and the structures of a number of them have been elucidated by the application of X-ray crystallography and other physical techniques. It is only necessary to consider these structures in outline in order to explain the ion-exchange properties of the clays; in this way we can see how they differ among themselves and what their relationship is to other types of inorganic ion exchange materials.

THE STRUCTURES OF CLAY MINERALS IN RELATION TO THEIR ION-EXCHANGE BEHAVIOUR

Basically the aluminosilicate "backbone" of the clays is composed of alternating, parallel, two-dimensional layers formed from silicate tetrahedra and aluminate octahedra[1]. The disposition of these layers and the extent and nature of isomorphous substitution within them determine to a great extent the chemical and physical properties of the material. Ideally we recognise three basic types of clay mineral (Fig. 1).

The simplest type (Fig. 1a) is characteristic of the kaolinite clays, which are found in china clay deposits; in this type the basic unit is a double layer consisting of one silicate and one aluminate layer with negligible isomorphous substitution in either of them. Units such as these are stacked together along the c-axis of the crystal, which is perpendicular to the layer planes, at the edges and corners of which there will normally be free hydroxyl groups. The basic formula for kaolinite is $Si_4Al_4O_{10}(OH)_8$, although individual mem-

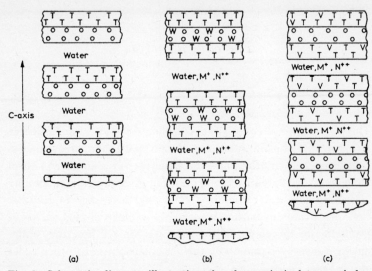

Fig. 1. Schematic diagram illustrating the three principal types of clay minerals. (a) Kaolinite; (b) Montmorillonite; (c) Illite. T = Tetrahedral silicate layers, O = Octahedral aluminate layers, V = Isomorphous substitution at tetrahedral sites, W = Isomorphous substitution at octahedral sites. M^+, N^{++}, balancing cations.

bers of the series may depart from this ideal composition. The free hydroxyl groups may exchange with anions when immersed in a salt solution; since they are weakly acid, the hydrogen in them may also exchange with cations. As a result, the material shows a small exchange capacity which is approximately the same for both anions and cations.

More complex types of clay mineral are based on a repeating unit consisting of one aluminate layer sandwiched between two silicate layers, the ideal basic formula being $Si_8Al_4O_{20}(OH)_4 \cdot nH_2O$. As a result of isomorphous substitution however, actual formulae differ widely from the latter, and two well-defined and distinct types may be recognized. Such substitution may occur in either the tetrahedral or the octahedral layer, depending upon the size and co-ordination number of the substituent ion in relation to those of aluminium and silicon. For example, Al^{+++} in the octahedral layer may be replaced by Mg^{++}, Fe^{++} and other octahedrally-coordinated ions of suitable radius, and Si^{++++} in the tetrahedral layer may be replaced by Al^{+++}, since the latter can exhibit a coordination number of either 4 or 6; aluminium is thus found in both tetrahedral and octahedral layers in some clays. In either case the parent ion is replaced by an ion of lower positive charge, and the "backbone" acquires a net unit negative charge for each such act of substitution; to preserve electroneutrality cations are incorporated into the interlayer spaces between each pair of triple units (Figs. 1b and 1c). When the mineral is suspended in an aqueous solution which can penetrate between the units these cations are freely mobile and can exchange with cations present in the solution. The cation exchange capacity of these two types thus arises partly from exchange at the edges and corners of sheets as in kaolinite, and to a much greater extent from the replacement of cations in the interlayer spaces; the extent of the latter will depend upon the degree of isomorphous substitution, but is normally much greater than that of the former. As a consequence of this, the cation ex-

TABLE 3

CATION-EXCHANGE CAPACITIES OF SOME CLAY MINERALS

Type	Mineral	Capacity meq/g
Kaolinite group	Kaolinite	0.02–0.10
Illite group	Muscovite	0.105
	Illite	0.13–0.42
Fibrous clays	Attapulgite	0.18–0.22
Montmorillonite group	Nontronite	0.57–0.64
	Saponite	0.69–0.81
	Montmorillonite	0.8–1.5
Micaceous derivatives	Biotite	0.03
	Vermiculite (pure)	1.0–1.5

These values are representative of a number of samples, but wide variations are possible for a given mineral depending upon its source and precise composition. In some cases where edge and corner exchange is appreciable, the capacity depends markedly upon particle size, *e.g.* kaolinite and illite; where exchange principally involves interlayer cations the effect of particle size is small.

References p. 41

change capacity of these two types of mineral greatly exceeds their anion exchange capacity (Table 3). Furthermore, while the cation exchange capacity of kaolinite may be increased considerably if the particle size is reduced by grinding, that of the other types of clay is much less dependent on this parameter.

In the kaolinite clays the forces between the individual units in the direction of the c-axis are weak Van der Waals and hydrogen-bonding forces, and consequently the minerals are readily dispersed in water, although flocculation may occur in salt solutions (p. 34). Isomorphous substitution in the octahedral layers, as in the mont-morillonite clays, together with the introduction of cations into the interlayer spaces, increases the strength of bonding along the c-axis by virtue of the electrostatic forces which are produced, although these are screened to some extent by the intervening tetrahedral layers. Although these clays do not disperse readily in water, they swell on immersion in aqueous solutions, the degree of swelling (and therefore the value of the c-axis spacing) depending upon the size of the cation entering the structure. Although swelling is normally reversible, if the cation is too large the attractive forces are overcome, the clay swells irreversibly and is said to be deflocculated. This type of clay includes the bentonites, mont-morillonite clays and Fullers' Earth.

When substitution occurs in the tetrahedral layers, as in illite and muscovite, the electrostatic forces between the negatively-charged "backbone" and the balancing cations are much stronger than in the montmorillonite group. Consequently the structure resists expansion on immersion in aqueous solutions and there is usually little change in the c-axis spacing (see, however, p. 40). The resistance to swelling generally leads to a low rate of exchange, and large cations may even be excluded on steric grounds; it is note-worthy, for example, that the cations present in naturally-occurring minerals of this class are the smaller ones such as potassium.

Unlike the zeolites (p. 43), exchange in the clay minerals is non-stoichiometric, and the capacity may vary appreciably among minerals having similar structures but showing different degrees of isomorphous substitution, and which may be found in different localities. We must also distinguish carefully between saturation capacity, equilibrium uptake, and rate of exchange. The saturation capacity depends upon the chemical composition of the clay and for cations decreases in the order montmorillonite > illite > kaolinite (Table 3). The uptake is an equilibrium property and depends upon the exchange thermodynamics and the solution composition and concentration; unlike the saturation capacity, it will depend upon the cation chosen and upon the cationic form of the clay with which it is equilibrated. The rate of exchange is a kinetic property which depends upon the surface area of the solid and the rate of diffusion of cations from solution into the latter and *vice versa*. Owing to the ready dispersion of kaolinite in suspensions and the mechanism of surface exchange which it exhibits, and because of the resistance to swelling of the illite group, cation exchange rates follow the order kaolinite > montmorillonite ≫ illite.

The clay minerals lose water when they are heated, reversibly at low temperatures and irreversibly at higher ones; as the temperature is increased the water which is lost arises successively from mobile water in the interlayer spaces, hydration water accompanying the exchangeable cations, and finally structural water from the backbone. Reversible loss of water is not accompanied by a change in exchange capacity, but the latter decreases permanently when water is lost irreversibly, and when structural water is lost from hydroxyl groups the lattice ultimately collapses and the cations are firmly bound within the backbone itself, and are very resistant to leaching except by reagents which attack the structure. The temperature at which fixation of cations occurs is generally lower when the radius of the unhydrated cation is small, since such cations are more readily incorporated into a collapsed structure, but is generally within the range 500–1000 °C (Fig. 2).

A similar "fixation" is observed even at ordinary temperatures in the case of certain cations (K^+, Rb^+, Cs^+) exchanged on non-expanding minerals such as illite, muscovite and vermiculite[2]. In these, after initial uptake in the interlayer spaces the cation may slowly penetrate into the tetrahedral layer, where it is inert towards replacement. The property of "potassium fixation" shown by cer-

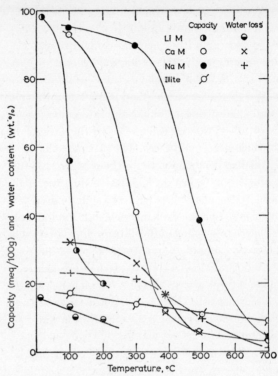

Fig. 2. Exchange capacity and loss of water in different cationic forms of clays after heating. (M = Montmorillonite) [Reproduced, with permission, from *Endeavour*, 17 (1958) 152.]

tain soils, which has important agricultural implications, is due, at least in part, to the presence in the soil of such minerals[3]. The question of this type of fixation in the non-expanding clay minerals is considered in more detail later (p. 32).

SELECTIVITY AND EXCHANGE EQUILIBRIA ON CLAYS:
EXCHANGE ON MONTMORILLONITE AND ATTAPULGITE

As in the case of organic ion exchange resins, well-defined affinity series are also observed in the clay minerals[4]; in general the affinity for cations increases in the order of decreasing hydrated-ion radius. In the alkali metals, for example, the order is

$$Li^+ < Na^+ < K^+ < Rb^+ < Cs^+.$$

The position of hydrogen ion in the series is difficult to determine, since treatment with acid generally results in breakdown of the aluminosilicate backbone, with dispersion of the clay and liberation of aluminium ions to the solution; the results obtained by titrating clays with acids should therefore be treated with reserve. Hydrogen forms of clay minerals may however be prepared by slurrying the latter with a cation-exchange resin in the hydrogen form; in order to maintain an approximately neutral pH in solution the resin is usually employed as a mixture with an anion exchange resin.

Precise thermodynamic data on ion exchange in clay systems could not be obtained until materials of reproducible composition were available, and the first work in this field was reported in 1951; since that date a series of papers by H. C. Thomas and his co-workers has provided information on a number of well-charac-terized clay minerals supplied by the American Petroleum Institute. The results are based upon uptake and elution curves obtained with mixed clay-asbestos columns in which the mineral is converted from one cationic form to another by solutions of varying composition. The methods adopted to study the exchange reactions can be divided into three types. Firstly, by studying the conversion of the natural clay (usually in the calcium or magnesium form, depending upon the particular mineral chosen) into a given cationic form, *e.g.* the caesium form by passing a caesium solution through the column, it is possible to measure the saturation capacity of the mineral both from the release of cations to the solution and from the amount of caesium taken up by the column. Secondly, by studying the exchange between the mono-ionic caesium clay and, say, potassium over several cycles of exchange, the reversibility of exchange can be demonstrated. As an extension of this study, purely isotopic exchange between an inactive caesium clay and a caesium solution traced with ^{137}Cs will give information on the kinetics of the exchange reaction uncomplicated by factors arising from the free energy of the exchange, since the latter is small for the isotopic system. Finally, in order to study the equilibrium between two cations A+ and B+, mixed solutions of constant total concentration and varying proportions of the two cations may be passed through the column until the influent and effluent compositions are identical. The clay is then in equilibrium with the two cations under the conditions obtaining in the feed solution, and the uptakes corresponding to these concentrations are obtainable by either integration under the breakthrough curve or elution of the cations from the clay and analysis of the eluent solution. Since the total solution concentration in the breakthrough experiment is fixed, it is only necessary to analyse for one of the ions in such an experiment, usually by means of a suitable radioactive tracer. In some instances, however, both cations have been traced in this way, and this leads to more accurate results if the affinity of the clay towards the two cations differs greatly.

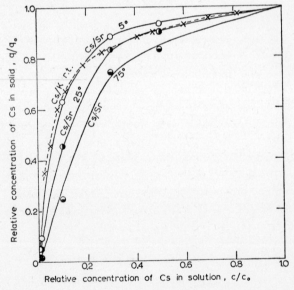

Fig. 3. Caesium–strontium and caesium–potassium isotherms on montmorillonite[5]. – – – – Cs/K, 0.01–0.04 N at room temperature (r.t.); ——— Cs/Sr, 0.05 N at temperatures shown.

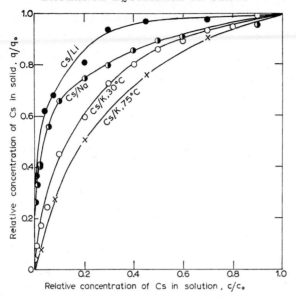

Fig. 4. Alkali metal exchange isotherms on attapulgite[6]. Solution concentration 0.02 N.

If q_0 is the saturation capacity of the clay, q the amount of a given ion absorbed at equilibrium, c_0 the total concentration of the solution employed and c the concentration of the ion in question, the results may be expressed as an isotherm in which the relative uptake q/q_0 is plotted as a function of the relative concentration c/c_0. The capacity and uptake are usually expressed in milliequivalents (meq) per gram of exchanger and the concentrations in meq per ml of solution. Typical isotherms for certain systems on the minerals montmorillonite[5] and attapulgite[6] are shown in Figs. 3 and 4.

The montmorillonite used in this work was from Chambers, Arizona, and its chemical composition corresponded to the formula

$$(Al_{1.329}Fe^{III}_{0.216}Mg_{0.541}Fe^{II}_{0.076})$$
$$(Si_{3.798}Al_{0.202})O_{10}(OH)_2(Ca_{0.209}Na_{0.029}K_{0.023})$$

in which the first bracket represents octahedrally-coordinated ions,

References p. 41

the second tetrahedrally-coordinated ions and the last exchangeable
cations; the calculated exchange capacity of 1.32 meq per gram of
backbone agrees well with the experimental value of 1.38. Comparison with the ideal formula given on p. 16 shows that isomorphous replacement has occurred in both the octahedral and
tetrahedral layers, but principally in the former. Attapulgite is a
fibrous clay mineral, in which there is some replacement of silicon
by aluminium in the tetrahedral layers, the octahedral layers containing both aluminium and magnesium; the excess negative charge
on the tetrahedral layer is partially balanced by a positive charge
on the octahedral layer, and the net exchange capacity (largely
Ca^{++}) is 0.2–0.3 meq/g. The composition of the particular sample
used in this work is less certain than that of the montmorillonite,
owing to the presence of an uncertain proportion of non-exchanging
impurities, and is therefore not quoted.

This method has also been used in a study of the clay mineral
fraction of a soil from the English Lower Greensand series[7]; in this
instance the soil was sieved to a fine mesh and any organic matter
destroyed by boiling with peroxide. Some typical results are shown
in Fig. 5. The significant features of these curves, which may be
expressed quantitatively as shown below, are (*i*) the existence of well-
defined affinity series and (*ii*) in soils where the exchange properties
are predominantly due to clay minerals the overall properties
are those to be expected on the basis of the behaviour of the individual
clays.

If we consider the exchange between a cation A^+ on the clay
and another cation B^+ in solution, using bars to represent the solid
phase, we may write the equilibrium as follows:

$$\overline{A}^+ + B^+ \rightleftharpoons A^+ + \overline{B}^+,$$

where the thermodynamic equilibrium constant is given by

$$K = \frac{\{A^+\}\,\{\overline{B}^+\}}{\{\overline{A}^+\}\,\{B^+\}} = \frac{[A^+]\,[\overline{B}^+]}{[\overline{A}^+]\,[B^+]}\,\frac{\Gamma_B}{\Gamma_A}\,\frac{\gamma_A}{\gamma_B} \tag{1}$$

In this expression $\{A^+\}$, $\{B^+\}$... represent thermodynamic activities, $[A^+]$, $[B^+]$... are concentrations, Γ_A and Γ_B are individual

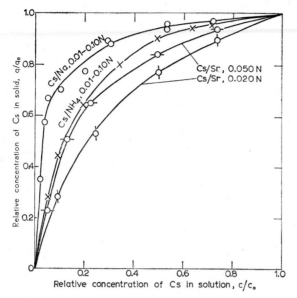

Fig. 5. Exchange isotherms on a Lower Greensand soil at 20 °C[7].
[Reproduced, with permission, from *Endeavour*, 17 (1958) 153.]

ion activity coefficients in the solid phase, and γ_A and γ_B activity coefficients in solution. The expression $[A^+]\,[\overline{B^+}]/[\overline{A^+}]\,[B^+]$ is the selectivity quotient $K_A{}^B$, which indicates the experimentally-observed extent to which the ion B^+ can displace A^+ under given conditions; hence

$$K = K_A{}^B \frac{\Gamma_B}{\Gamma_A} \frac{\gamma_A}{\gamma_B} \qquad (2)$$

In the solution phase we may replace the ratio γ_A/γ_B by $\gamma_{\pm(AX)}/\gamma_{\pm(BX)}$, where X^- is the anion employed; data for $\gamma_\pm$ are frequently available for simple salt solutions, either singly or mixed, and in the former case standard treatments may be applied to obtain values in mixed solutions. In this way we may derive $K' = K_A{}^B \cdot \gamma_A/\gamma_B$, whence

$$K = K' \cdot \Gamma_B/\Gamma_A \qquad (3)$$

Similar treatments may be applied to derive K' if the charges on A and B are different.

Using data for [A$^+$], [B$^+$], [$\overline{A}^+$] and [$\overline{B}^+$] from isotherms such as those in Figs. 3–5 and existing activity coefficient data, we may thus arrive at values of K', but further treatment is necessary in order to derive the thermodynamic constant K.

The latter was derived from first principles by Gaines and Thomas[8], assuming the exchanger to consist of a solid aluminosilicate backbone possessing a fixed number of cation exchange sites and capable of absorbing water but not anions from the surrounding medium. In the general case where exchange involves cations A^{x+} and B^{y+} with charges x and y respectively, the equilibrium constant is given by the expression

$$\ln K = (y - x) + \ln \frac{\Gamma_A^y(a)}{\Gamma_B^x(b)} + \int_0^1 \ln K' \cdot dN_B - xy \int_a^b n_s \cdot d\ln a_s \quad (4)$$

where Γ and K' are defined as above, N_B is the equivalent fraction of B in the exchanger, n_s is the water content of one exchange equivalent of the solid and a_s the water activity. Of the four terms in eqn. (4) the first is readily calculated and the third may be obtained by integrating below the curve of $\ln K'$ as a function of N_B, the latter being identical with q/q_0. Of the other two terms, the second represents the contribution to the free energy of the reaction due to the two clays in their pure mono-ionic forms being brought from infinitely dilute solutions of the respective ions to the appropriate equilibrium solutions, while the fourth represents the contribution due to the change in water activity in the solid on passing from a solution containing the ions B$^+$ only to one containing A$^+$. Since the second and fourth terms may usually be neglected in comparison with the third, within the limits of experimental accuracy, the expression (4) may be simplified as follows according to the magnitude of the charges on A and B:

(a) Ions A$^+$ and B$^+$ ($x = y = 1$)

$$\ln K = \int_0^1 \ln K' \cdot dN_B = \int_0^1 \ln K_A^B \cdot dN_B + \int_0^1 \ln \frac{\gamma_A}{\gamma_B} \cdot dN_B$$

(b) Ions A^{++} and B$^+$ ($x = 2, y = 1$)

$$\ln K = -1 + \int_0^1 \ln K' \cdot dN_B$$

$$= -1 + \int_0^1 \ln K_A{}^B \cdot dN_B + \int_0^1 \ln \frac{\gamma_A}{\gamma_B{}^2} \cdot dN_B$$

(c) Ions A^{+++} and B^+ $(x = 3, y = 1)$

$$\ln K = -2 + \int_0^1 \ln K' \cdot dN_B$$

$$= -2 + \int_0^1 \ln K_A{}^B \cdot dN_B + \int_0^1 \ln \frac{\gamma_A}{\gamma_B{}^3} \cdot dN_B$$

In this way Thomas and his co-workers have obtained thermodynamic equilibrium constants, free energies and entropies of exchange for a number of $1:1$, $1:2$ and $1:3$ exchange systems on the
minerals montmorillonite[5,10] and attapulgite[6], and by working at
different temperatures they have calculated heats of exchange using
the Van 't Hoff isochore. The data in Table 4, which include also
values for a Lower Greensand soil[7], give quantitative expression to
the affinity series derived by earlier workers, and show that in general
the free energies and heats of exchange are small, in common with
many ion-exchange reactions. The thermodynamic equilibrium constant is independent of total ionic concentration in all cases, but this
is not true for the selectivity quotient $K_A{}^B$ unless the charges on A
and B are identical. As a consequence of the law of mass action, exchange favours the more highly-charged ion when the total salt concentration is decreased, and this results in a displacement of the
isotherm as shown in Fig. 3 for caesium and strontium. Calculations of
$K_A{}^B$ as a function of exchanger composition, and of the activity
coefficients of the individual cations in the solid phase, show that the
system is non-ideal, the deviations from ideality being least for exchange between ions of similar charge and size. For example, the exchange
between calcium and barium ions on montmorillonite gives a linear
isotherm, with $K_{Ca}{}^{Ba} = 1$ between 20° and 70 °C at total concentrations between 0.02 and 0.05 N[9]. Since the water contents of

TABLE 4

THERMODYNAMIC DATA FOR EXCHANGE ON CLAYS

Exchanger	System	K	ΔG^0 kcal $\cdot$ mole^{-1}	ΔH^0 kcal $\cdot$ mole^{-1}	Ref.
Attapulgite	$Li^+ \to Cs^+$	0.029 (30°)	2.14		
		0.068 (75°)		4.1	
	$Na^+ \to Cs^+$	0.041 (30°)	1.93		
		0.090 (75°)		3.8	6
	$K^+ \to Cs^+$	0.131 (30°)	1.22		
		0.243 (75°)		2.9	
Montmorillonite	$K^+ \to Cs^+$	0.076 (20°)	1.5	—	5
	$Sr^{2+} \to Cs^+$	1.9×10^{-3} (25°)	3.7		
		7.2×10^{-3} (75°)		6.5	5
	$Y^{3+} \to Cs^+$	3.8×10^{-4} (30°)	4.7		
		15.9×10^{-4} (75°)		6.6	10
Lower Greensand soil (clay fraction)	$Na^+ \to Cs^+$	0.057 (20°)	1.85	—	
	$NH_4^+ \to Cs^+$	0.128 (20°)	1.19	—	7
	$Sr^{2+} \to Cs^+$	6.4×10^{-4} (20°)	3.89	—	

(The convention $A^+ \to B^+$ represents ion A^+ displacing ion B^+ from the clay, *i.e.* the equilibrium represented is $A^+ + BX \rightleftharpoons AX + B^+$, where X is the exchanger backbone)

the clay were found to be equal in both calcium and barium forms, the thermodynamic equilibrium constant must also be unity. At 220 °C, however, barium is absorbed slightly more strongly than is calcium, with $K_{Ca}^{Ba} = 1.2$ and $\Delta H \approx 0.3$ kcal $\cdot$ mole^{-1}. In contrast to this near-ideal behaviour, the exchange between caesium and the trivalent cerium or yttrium ion on montmorillonite is unusually complex, and shows reversals of selectivity as a function of exchanger composition which depend upon the total composition and the temperature[10]; the sigmoid isotherms which result

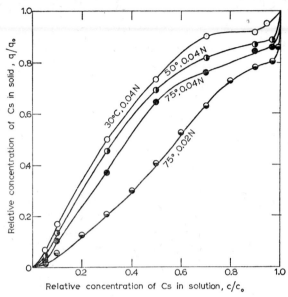

Fig. 6. Caesium–yttrium isotherms on montmorillonite[10].

(Fig. 6) resemble those obtained with certain zeolites (p. 60) and with zirconium phosphate (p. 125). The reasons for this behaviour are not clear, but it may result from repulsive interaction between neighbouring ions leading to less favourable exchange when numbers of the sites are occupied by such highly-charged species. In the simpler cases of pairs of alkali metal cations on montmorillonite and on attapulgite a smaller degree of non-ideality is observed in the solid phase, but appreciable deviations are observed for ions of unlike charge such as Cs^+ and Sr^{++}; no reversals of selectivity have been observed in these cases, however, and simple rectilinear isotherms are obtained.

EXCHANGE IN MICA AND VERMICULITE

Both structurally and from the viewpoint of ion exchange the micaceous minerals are of interest as precursors of the typical clay minerals, which may be derived from them by weathering processes, vermiculite representing an intermediate stage in the conversion of mica to clay. In mica isomorphous replacement of Si^{IV} by Al^{III} occurs in the tetrahedral layers and is balanced by potassium ions located in the interlayer spaces; swelling is negligible, but potassium ions are liberated when muscovite mica is soaked in $(NH_4)_2SO_4$ solution[11]; the extent of this exchange depends upon the particle size and the rate of exchange is very small[12]. Although the capacity appears also to be dependent upon particle size it is still not clear whether the lattice is penetrated, or whether exchange can only occur at cleavage surfaces.

In a preliminary study[13] of a Bengal Ruby muscovite mica having a composition close to the ideal formula $KAl_2(AlSi_3)O_{10}(OH)_2$, wet ground fractions of different particle size were equilibrated with traced salt solutions to replace potassium ions, after which the displacing cation was equilibrated with a suitable cation-exchange membrane and the cation transport to the membrane determined. The hydrogen form of the mica, prepared by equilibration with a cation-exchange membrane in the hydrogen form, was also titrated with salt solutions under nitrogen. The results showed that potassium could be displaced by an equivalent amount of caesium without any change in surface area. Repeated isotopic exchange experiments with inactive and tracer-active caesium solutions showed a gradually decreasing uptake which was attributed to the preferential absorption of trace impurities, since the ^{137}Ba daughter of ^{137}Cs was absorbed more strongly than its parent. Exchange was rapid on the exposed surface of the particles, but penetration of unexposed cleavage planes was very slow, the times required to reach equilibrium in the two cases being minutes and days respectively; the measured capacity of 0.0015 meq/g for 40–60 mesh material may be compared with the theoretical maximum value of 3.48 calculated on the assumption that the cleavage of a mica sheet exposes one half of the interlayer potassium on each new surface. Exchange studies involving acid or alkaline solutions (as in the titration experiments) are limited by attack upon the backbone (Table 5), which liberates aluminium and silicon[14]; the amount

TABLE 5

RELEASE OF Al AND Si FROM MICA LEACHED WITH AQUEOUS
SOLUTIONS FOR 24 h AT 25°C[14]

Leaching solution	20–40 mesh		100–200 mesh	
	Al	Si	Al	Si
0.1 N HCl	300 μg	85 μg	1280 μg	380 μg
0.1 N KOH	140	310	300	470
0.1 N KCl	0	0	0	5
Water	0	5	5	10

of mica dissolved in these experiments ($< 1\%$) is more than suffi-
cient to saturate all the exchange sites. Acid attack appears to
be directed chiefly at the octahedral Al layers via their edges, while
the slower attack by alkali appears to occur at the tetrahedral Si_3Al
cleavage faces.

Vermiculite is important scientifically because it represents an
intermediate stage between the micas and typical expanding lattice
clay minerals such as montmorillonite; it also has an agricultural
and commercial importance, since it is a common soil mineral and
may be used for a variety of horticultural purposes. Commercial
vermiculite, as mined, is not unlike mica in appearance, but if
heated rapidly the water contained in it vaporizes within the particles and causes the grains to expand considerably in a direction
perpendicular to the lattice planes. The product is the well-known
"exfoliated vermiculite" used by seedsmen and horticultural spe-
cialists because of its high porosity to retain nutrient media for
plant growth. Because of its low density and thermal conductivity
it is also used as a heat-insulating medium.

Vermiculite is derived from the mica biotite which, like muscovite,
has a collapsed lattice with tetrahedral substitution and no interlayer water, the exchangeable cation being potassium. The structure of vermiculite is similar, but in this case the exchangeable
cations are magnesium and calcium, and interlayer water is also
present. Each may be converted into the other as follows:

$$\text{Biotite} \xrightleftharpoons[\text{KCl solution}]{\text{MgCl}_2 \text{ solution}} \text{Vermiculite}$$

The replacement of potassium in biotite by magnesium is however extremely slow, the process taking several months to reach equilibrium. Most commercial vermiculites are not true vermiculite, but are rather hydrobiotites, which are mixed-layer minerals containing both vermiculite and biotite structures in varying proportions; the exchangeable ions will thus be magnesium (or calcium) and potassium in proportions which are related to the proportions of vermiculite and biotite respectively and to the respective ion exchange capacities of the two minerals. To a first approximation, since the capacity of biotite is small, the ratio of the measured exchange capacity of the hydrobiotite to that of true vermiculite ($\sim$ 1.60 meq/g) is equal to the proportion of the latter in the mineral. The exchange properties of commercial vermiculites depend upon the cation being studied[15]; large ions (Mg^{++}, Ca^{++}, Li^+ and Na^+) exchange with the vermiculite layers only, without alteration in the c-axis spacing, while small ions such as K^+, NH_4^+, Rb^+ and Cs^+ can enter the biotite layers also. In addition, the latter ions, because of their smaller size and lesser degree of hydration, cause a collapse of the vermiculite layers and therefore a reduction in the c-axis dimensions. The uptake of small ions attains equilibrium more slowly because of the need to penetrate the non-expanding biotite layers, and although the exfoliated mineral exchanges more rapidly than natural vermiculite, the capacities are the same. The slow exchange in the biotite layers and the collapse of the vermiculite layers when small ions are exchanged have important consequences; the presence of vermiculite leads to fixation of these ions in soils[2] and the mineral can thus act as a reservoir of potassium which is released only slowly for plant nutrition. Vermiculite also displays striking selectivity towards certain cations, *e.g.* from a solution containing 0.1 N NaCl and 0.001 N CsCl a sample of South Carolina vermiculite was found to take up 96.2% Cs and 3.8% Na, equivalent to a selectivity quotient of $K_{Na}{}^{Cs} = 2400$. This property has led to the suggestion that vermiculite be used as an absorbent to remove cations from radioactive wastes. The high degree of selectivity towards caesium which is displayed by certain shales is attributed to a similar collapse of the lattice which is undergone by the illite present in them when caesium is absorbed[16].

Thermodynamic data have been reported[17] on a vermiculite having the composition

$$(K_{1.09}Na_{0.06}Mg_{0.415}) (Ti^{IV}_{0.11}Fe^{III}_{0.65}Mg^{II}_{5.24}) (Si^{IV}_{5.72}Al^{III}_{2.28}) O_{20.65}OH_{3.35} \; ;$$

the saturation capacity of 0.80 meq/g (corresponding to $\sim 50\%$ true vermiculite content) was increased on boiling with 0.2 M magnesium chloride solution to a value of 1.45 characteristic of a pure vermiculite. Using the lithium form, column exchange studies were carried out at temperatures up to 90 °C, and batch exchange studies up to 300 °C. Both neutral and basic solutions were investigated, and even in the latter at 300 °C no breakdown of the backbone was detected. Potassium uptake was found to be irreversible, but the lithium–sodium exchange was reversible in both neutral and alkaline solutions at all temperatures (Fig. 7); the selectivity

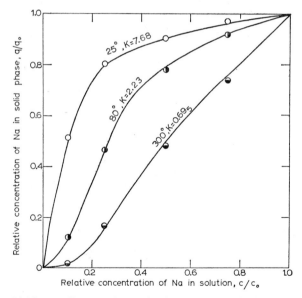

Fig. 7. Lithium–sodium exchange isotherms on vermiculite from 0.05 N neutral solution. [Reproduced, with permission, from *Bull. Serv. Carte Geol. Alsace Lorraine*, 14 (1961) 149.]

TABLE 6

THERMODYNAMIC DATA FOR Li/Na EXCHANGE ON VERMICULITE[17]

System	Solution concentration	Temperature °C	K
Li V + Na⁺	0.02 N	80	2.01
Na V + Li⁺	0.02 N	80	$0.49 = \dfrac{1}{2.03}$
Li V + Na⁺	0.05 N	25	7.68
		80	2.23
		300	0.69_5
Na V + Li⁺	0.05 N	80	$0.43 = \dfrac{1}{2.33}$

quotient decreased with increasing temperature, since at higher temperatures the ions will be less highly hydrated and the difference in ionic radii (and hence in affinities) will be smaller. Thermodynamic constants for the Li^+/Na^+ exchange are given in Table 6.

The kinetics of cation exchange on a sodium vermiculite have been shown[18] to be controlled by particle diffusion[19] and to be independent of solution concentration except at high values of the latter. The rate decreases in the order of increasing ionic size and for the alkaline earths may be correlated with changes in the entropy of hydration.

ION-EXCHANGE EQUILIBRIA IN KAOLINITE

Because of its low exchange capacity, and because the aggregation of particles varies with the composition of the solutions with which it is brought into contact, conventional column or batch exchange methods are unsuitable for studying equilibria involving kaolinite. To overcome these difficulties, Tamers and Thomas passed the exchanging solution slowly through a continuously-stirred suspension, thus maintaining the external solution composition approximately constant[20]; cation and anion exchange were followed simultaneously using alkali halide solutions. Although isotopic exchange experi-

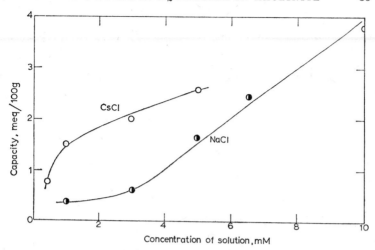

Fig. 8. Cation exchange capacity of kaolinite suspensions as a function of the nature and concentration of the equilibrating solution[20]. [Reproduced, with permission, from *J. Phys. Chem.*, 64 (1960) 29.]

ments showed that instantaneous equilibrium between solution and solid was rapidly established, the measured capacity decreased on standing, and the final value was found to be a function of the nature and concentration of the cation employed. (Fig. 8). These results are explicable on the basis of exchange occurring at sites on the edges and faces of the crystallites, since the capacity will then vary with the degree of flocculation; on standing in contact with a salt solution the particles will slowly aggregate, with a corresponding decrease in the number of sites and hence a release of cations to the solution. On increasing the salt concentration the degree of aggregation will decrease, leading to an increased capacity, and this effect will be more marked in the case of caesium ions than for sodium ions, because of the greater selectivity of the clay for the former. The fact that cation and anion exchange capacities increase together as the salt concentration is increased supports the view that exchange occurs on surface sites, but the departure from a simple 1:1 relationship between anion and cation exchange capacities indicates that this simple model is not quantitatively exact. Qualitative differences in the shapes of the curves for caesium and sodium chlorides have been tentatively explained in terms of differing modes of aggregation releasing different numbers of sites on deflocculation, but the data are insufficient to permit a precise interpretation to be made.

The differences between cation and anion exchange behaviour may also be explained by assuming that the former involves exchange arising from a small degree of isomorphous replacement as well as exchange at surface hydroxyl groups, while the latter is due to surface exchange only. There has been for several years an alternative hypothesis[21] which ascribes cation exchange in kaolinite to a small but measurable degree of isomorphous replacement, and more recent measurements on talc and pyrophyllite support this view[22]. Talc has the ideal formula $Mg_3Si_4O_{10}(OH)_2$ and, in the sample chosen, replacement of silicon by aluminium and iron had taken place, accompanied by the presence of sodium and potassium as balancing cations. Samples converted to the hydrogen form by electrodialysis gave, on titration with sodium hydroxide, a capacity of 0.0023 meq/g, independent of particle size. Kaolinite and pyrophyllite, however, displayed capacities of 0.01–0.06 and 0.04 meq/g respectively, both dependent on particle size. The latter mineral has a structure resembling that of talc, except that aluminium replaces magnesium. The fact that aluminium (ionic radius 0.57 Å) can replace silicon (0.57 Å) in the tetrahedral layers whereas magnesium (0.78 Å) can not, is held to be responsible for the greater capacities of kaolinite and pyrophyllite relative to that of talc. While the evidence to date is insufficient to decide between the two alternative mechanisms, it seems likely that in kaolinite at least both may be operative.

ORGANIC DERIVATIVES OF CLAY MINERALS

Organic cations such as alkyl-substituted ammonium ions may also exchange with suitable clays if steric considerations permit, to give a wide range of materials which absorb gases very efficiently. While the clays normally do not absorb non-polar molecules, the introduction of an organic cation can bring this about in two different ways. Small, nearly spherical cations, such as the tetra-alkylammonium ions NR_4^+, hold the lattice layers apart at a distance approximately equal to the ionic diameter, with about the same distance between individual cations; the interlamellar free space thus created provides channels in which the permanent gases, paraffins and aromatic hydrocarbons may be absorbed if space permits. Secondly, the exchange of long-chain mono-alkylammonium ions NH_3R^+, while filling the interlamellar spaces, can lead to sorption of hydrocarbons by the intermingling of the chains of the latter with those of the exchangeable cation. The difference between the two types of sorption is revealed in the different shapes of the isotherms in the two cases[23] (Fig. 9). The steric factors involved permit suitable organic clay derivatives to be used for the chromatographic separation of hydrocarbons, and the high de-

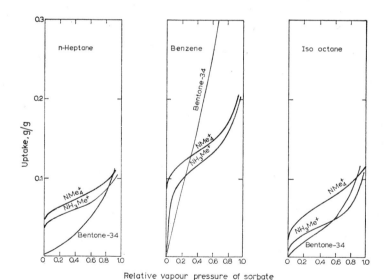

Fig. 9. Adsorption isotherms for *n*-heptane, benzene and iso-octane on tetramethylammonium, methylammonium and dimethyldioctadecylammonium montmorillonites[23]. [Reproduced, with permission, from *Trans. Faraday Soc.*, 57 (1961) 452.]

gree of specificity makes it possible in some cases to separate isomers, *e.g.* the xylenes. The uptake of long-chain alkylammonium ions by clays causes the latter to become progressively less hydrophilic as the chain length of the alkyl substituent is increased, and for chain lengths of the order of 8–10 carbon atoms the clay becomes so organophilic that the uptake of cations from solution considerably exceeds the saturation capacity[24]. It has been shown that in the latter case the excess is held as the free amine, presumably by Van der Waals forces, the reactions involved being as follows:

(a) uptake to saturation capacity:

$$MX + RNH_3^+ \rightleftharpoons M^+ + RNH_3X$$

(b) uptake in excess of saturation capacity:

$$RNH_3X + RNH_3^+ \rightleftharpoons [RNH_3X]RNH_2 + H^+$$

The existence of reaction (b) is indicated by a decrease in the pH of the solution due to the hydrogen ion liberated when the saturation capacity is exceeded.

SWELLING IN RELATION TO THE EXCHANGE PROPERTIES OF CLAY MINERALS

The ability to swell in water is governed largely by the interlamellar cation density, which often dominates the ease of exchange, since the forces between the lamellae will depend to a large extent upon the number of cations per unit area of the sheets. Table 7 illustrates the fact that as the area per cation increases, so does the extent of swelling and of exchange; when the concentration of interlayer cations is very high (as in the micas) or nearly zero (as in pyrophyllite) exchange and swelling are both very small. For a clay of moderately high cation density and good swelling properties, such as montmorillonite, the degree of swelling in salt solutions increases approximately as $C^{-\frac{1}{2}}$, where C is the aqueous concentra-

TABLE 7

DENSITY OF INTERLAYER CATIONS IN CLAY MINERALS IN RELATION
TO SWELLING IN DISTILLED WATER

[R. M. Barrer, *Chem. Ind. (London)*, (1962) 1258]

Mineral	Area per cation Å^2	Swelling in water, Å	
		Na$^+$-*form*	Ca^{2+}-*form*
Margarite	12	0	0
Muscovite	24	1.9	2.8
Glauconite	31	3.8	2.8
Illite	32	4.2	2.8
Vermiculite	36	5.1	4.3
Nontronite	46	∞	9.2
Montmorillonite	75	∞	9.6
Hectorite	100	∞	10.6
Pyrophyllite	∞	0	0

tion. When organic cations are introduced into clays, the manner in which the former are accommodated, and hence the degree of swelling, depend upon the relationship between the area available per cation (as calculated from the exchange capacity) and the geometrical area of the latter. If the available area is comparable with the ionic surface area the cations will be stacked parallel to the planes, but as the available area decreases relative to the ionic size the cations are inclined at an increasing angle to the planes, until finally in the extreme case they are stacked vertically. For long-chain organic cations stacked in this way the degree of swelling may be very great. The ability of such derivatives to imbibe organic liquids (see above) renders some of them of great use as thickeners and gelling agents, *e.g.* Bentone–34, dimethyl dioctadecylammonium bentonite, derived from bentonite, a member of the montmorillonite group.

It is interesting to note that long-chain organic cations can completely replace the interlayer cations even in the micas, albeit slowly, and that the organic mica derivatives display a much higher capacity for inorganic cations than do the original micas, since exchange is aided by the greater degree of separation in the organic derivatives (Table 8).

TABLE 8

EXCHANGE CAPACITIES AND SWELLING BEHAVIOUR OF SOME MICACEOUS MINERALS

[A. Weiss, *Z. Anorg. Allgem. Chem.*, 297 (1958) 17]

Mineral	Cation present in natural mineral	Exchange capacity		Cationic form in which mineral swells in water or organic liquids
		Inorganic ions	Long-chain amines or diamines	
Margarite	Ca^{++}	$\leqslant 5$	$\leqslant 380$	$[NH_3(CH_2)_xNH_3]^{++}$, $x > 10$
Muscovite Biotite	K^+ (Na^+, Li^+)	$\leqslant 5$	$\leqslant 250$	$[NH_3(CH_2)_xNH_3]^{++}$ $(x > 8)$ RNH_3^+, $R_2NH_2^+$ below 30 °C Inorganic ions except K^+, NH_4^+, Rb^+, Cs^+, Tl^+
Illite	K^+ (Na^+, Li^+)	$\leqslant 35$	$\leqslant 200$	As in muscovite
Vermiculite	Mg^{++}, Ca^{++} (Na^+)	100–170	100–170	All cations except K^+, NH_4^+, Rb^+, Cs^+, Tl^+
Montmorillonite	Mg^{++}, Ca^{++}, $Na^+(K^+)$	60–120	60–120	All cations

PROPOSALS FOR UTILISATION OF CLAYS AS ION-EXCHANGE MEDIA

Although their stability towards acid solutions is limited, suggestions have been made that the clay minerals be used as ion exchange media in certain cases, particularly where specificity, cheapness, or stability towards radiation or high-temperature water is concerned. Montmorillonite has been suggested for the treatment of radioactive waste solutions, but because of its small particle size some preliminary treatment is necessary to produce material capable of being used in large columns. Two processes which have been examined involve either extrusion from an aqueous slurry into the ion exchange column[25] or incorporation of a binder such as ethyl orthosilicate, which is subsequently decomposed by firing with some loss in capacity[26]. Both these methods have their disadvantages, and neither product is stable physically in aqueous solutions at high temperatures. In a third process[27] montmorillonite is alternatively washed in dilute acid and alkaline solutions, and the particles of diameter $< 2\mu$ are separated, flocculated at pH 1 and centrifuged; a 2% suspension is then electrodialysed for about three weeks in distilled water to remove all chloride ion, after which the suspension is slowly evaporated to dryness at 70 °C. The solid is then crushed and sieved to give a product consisting of oriented aggregates in which the crystal planes are parallel to the lamellae; alternatively the flocculate may be partially dried and extruded to give filaments having 50% humidity. It is claimed that the aggregates (which are in the hydrogen form) are physically stable in aqueous solutions at 300 °C, and that their hydrogen ions can be replaced reversibly by other cations. The capacity for barium is quoted as ~ 1 meq/g at both 100 ° and 250 °C.

Vermiculite also shows promise for this type of application, and has the advantage that no preparation is necessary; in order to achieve the best possible exchange rates the exfoliated form should be used.

REFERENCES

1 R. E. GRIM, *Clay Mineralogy*, McGraw-Hill, London, 1953.
2 I. BARSHAD, *Am. Mineralogist*, 33 (1948) 655; 34 (1949) 675.
3 J. C. MARTIN, R. OVERSTREET AND D. R. HOAGLAND, *Soil Sci. Soc. Am. Proc.*, 10 (1946) 94.
4 P. SCHACHTSCHABEL, *Kolloid-Beih.*, 51 (1940) 199.
5 J. A. FAUCHER, R. W. SOUTHWORTH AND H. C. THOMAS, *J. Chem. Phys.*, 20 (1952) 157; J. A. FAUCHER AND H. C. THOMAS, *J. Chem. Phys.*, 22 (1954) 258; G. L. GAINES AND H. C. THOMAS, *J. Chem. Phys.*, 23 (1955) 2322.
6 C. N. MERRIAM AND H. C. THOMAS, *J. Chem. Phys.*, 24 (1956) 993.
7 C. B. AMPHLETT AND L. A. MCDONALD, *J. Inorg. Nucl. Chem.*, 2 (1956) 403; 6 (1958) 145.
8 G. L. GAINES AND H. C. THOMAS, *J. Chem. Phys.*, 21 (1953) 714. Similar results have been obtained by less rigorous treatments by ARGERSINGER, DAVIDSON AND BONNER, *Trans. Kansas Acad. Sci.*, 53 (1950) 404; EKEDAHL, HÖGFELDT AND SILLÉN, *Acta Chem. Scand.*, 4 (1950) 556.

9 J. P. LEIBENGUTH AND R. WEY, *Compt. Rend.*, 251 (1960) 715.

10 G. R. FRYSINGER AND H. C. THOMAS, *J. Phys. Chem.*, 64 (1960) 224.

11 R. F. GARDINER AND E. C. SHOREY, *J. Ind. Eng. Chem.*, 9 (1917) 589; M. L. JACKSON AND E. TRUOG, *Soil Sci. Soc. Am. Proc.*, 4 (1939) 136.

12 W. P. KELLEY AND H. JENNY, *Soil Sci.*, 41 (1936) 367; P. SCHACHTSCHA-BEL, *Kolloid-Beih.*, 51 (1940) 199.

13 G. L. GAINES, *J. Phys. Chem.*, 61 (1957) 1408.

14 G. L. GAINES AND C. P. RUTKOWSKI, *J. Phys. Chem.*, 61 (1957) 1439.

15 G. R. FRYSINGER, *Proc. Natl. Conf. Clays and Clay Minerals*, 8 (1960) 116.

16 T. TAMURA AND D. G. JACOBS, *Health Phys.*, 2 (1960) 391.

17 E. WILHELM, *Thesis*, Strasbourg, 1962.

18 J. KEAY AND A. WILD, *Soil Sci.*, 92 (1961) 54.

19 J. A. KITCHENER, *Ion-Exchange Resins*, Methuen, London, 1957, ch. 4.

20 M. A. TAMERS AND H. C. THOMAS, *J. Phys. Chem.*, 64 (1960) 29.

21 R. H. S. ROBERTSON, G. W. BRINDLEY AND R. C. MACKENZIE, *Am. Mineralogist*, 39 (1954) 118.

22 W. D. KINGERY, F. A. HALDEN AND C. R. KURKIJAN, *J. Phys. Chem.*, 59 (1955) 378.

23 R. M. BARRER AND K. E. KELSEY, *Trans. Faraday Soc.*, 57 (1961) 452, 625.

24 C. T. COWAN AND D. WHITE, *Trans. Faraday Soc.*, 54 (1958) 691.

25 L. P. HATCH, *Am. Scientist*, 41 (1953) 410; W. S. GINELL, J. J. MARTIN AND L. P. HATCH, *Nucleonics*, 12 (12) (1954) 14.

26 T. BEIRNE, J. R. GROVER AND J. M. HUTCHEON, *U.K.A.E.A. Report AERE* CE/R-1658, (1955).

27 C.E.A., French Patent No. 1,208,497 (1960); R. PLATZER AND R. BITTEL, *Silicates Ind.*, 24 (1959) 550.

CHAPTER 3

The zeolites

The zeolites form another group of aluminosilicate minerals, the structures of which are built up from tetrahedral groupings having the formulae AlO_4^{5-} and SiO_4^{4-} in such a way that corners, edges and faces of the tetrahedra are shared to give condensed structures. Like the clays they possess well-defined crystal structures. Depending upon the structure and type of bonding, zeolites may exist as fibrous, lamellar, or rigid three-dimensional structures; the first two classes are analogous to the fibrous clays (*e.g.* attapulgite, sepiolite) and to the typical lamellar clays and micas respectively, but the third type, with strong covalent bonding in three dimensions, has no analogue in the clay series. It is this type of robust, three-dimensional network which is usually taken to represent the zeolites, and it is this type which has been extensively studied for its ion-exchange properties, particularly by Barrer and his co-workers[1]. Stoichiometrically the zeolites may be regarded as being derived from the formula $(SiO_2)_n$ by replacing silicon by aluminium to varying extents, the resulting net negative charge being balanced, as in the clays, by introducing an equivalent number of cations into the structure; water molecules may also be incorporated, as well as non-structural anions such as sulphate, carbonate and sulphide. Such a picture gives no idea of the structural complexities which may exist, neither does it hint at the finer details of the ion-exchange properties of these materials, which are considerably more complex than those of the clays. Although the two types of exchanger have many properties in common, the regular three-dimensional nature of the zeolites results in their possessing stoichiometric formulae, unlike the more irregular pattern which arises from the varying degrees of isomorphous sub-

TABLE 9

COMPOSITIONS AND EXCHANGE CAPACITIES FOR SELECTED ZEOLITES[1]

Zeolite	Composition	Exchange capacity meq/g
	(a) Fibrous zeolites	
Edingtonite	Ba $[Al_2Si_3O_{10}] \cdot 4H_2O$	3.90
Natrolite	$Na_2 [Al_2Si_3O_{10}] \cdot 2H_2O$	5.30
Scolecite	Ca $[Al_2Si_3O_{10}] \cdot 3H_2O$	5.00
	(b) Lamellar zeolites	
Stilbite	$(NaCa_{\frac{1}{2}}) [AlSi_3O_8] \cdot 3H_2O$	3.20
Heulandite	Ca $[Al_2Si_6O_{16}] \cdot 5H_2O$	3.30
	(c) Three-dimensional zeolites	
Analcite	Na $[AlSi_2O_6] \cdot H_2O$	4.50
Mordenite	$(Ca_{\frac{1}{2}}Na) [AlSi_5O_{12}] \cdot 3.3H_2O$	2.30
Chabazite	$(Ca_{\frac{1}{2}},Na) [AlSi_2O_6] \cdot 3H_2O$	4.00
Faujasite	$(Ca, Na_2) [Al_2Si_5O_{14}] \cdot 6.6H_2O$	3.90
	(d) Felspathoids	
Leucite	K $[AlSi_2O_6]$	4.60
Sodalite	Na $[AlSiO_4] \cdot 2/3NaCl$	9.20
Ultramarine	Na $[AlSiO_4] \cdot 1/3Na_2S_x$	8.30
Cancrinite	$(Na, Ca_{\frac{1}{2}}) [AlSiO_4] \cdot 2/3(Na_2, Ca)CO_3$	10.90

Notes (1) Capacities are based on hydrated formula weights.

(2) Framework compositions are given in square brackets [ ].

(3) Actual formulae may vary due to varying water content or to isomorphous replacements such as $NaAl \rightleftharpoons Si$.

stitution which are possible in the clays. Another consequence of their three-dimensional rigidity is that the lattice is unable to swell to accommodate ions above a certain size. Table 9 shows[1] a selection of typical zeolites together with their exchange capacities. Reference is made elsewhere (p. 87) to anion-exchanging mixed oxides which may formally be regarded as analogous to the zeolites.

When the structures of the zeolites are examined in detail[1] it is seen that the polyhedra are stacked in such a way that there are channels penetrating into the interior of the lattice; the channels may either be intersecting or non-intersecting, and they may either pass completely through the lattice or terminate within it. Their diameters are seen to vary from one type of structure to another, and may even vary along the length of an individual channel. Within the lattice there may also be approximately spherical cavities, which may be connected to the exterior by such channels. Within these cavities and channels are located the cations, nonstructural anions (if any) and any water molecules, and many variations are possible upon this theme. Obviously a cation present in the original structure when the zeolite is synthesised can only undergo ion exchange if a channel of suitable dimensions is available along which it can diffuse to the external solution; even then it will only exchange with ions which themselves have a diameter compatible with the channel diameter so that they can in turn diffuse from the solution into the structure. In addition to the restrictions placed upon the channel dimensions by structural considerations the available space may be further limited by the presence of water molecules or of anions within the channels; apart from purely thermodynamic factors controlling selectivity there are thus opportunities for a wide range of steric factors to modify or control the behaviour of the exchanger. The range of channel diameters found in the zeolite series is a wide one, and in some instances there may in addition be an appreciable difference between maximum and minimum dimensions for a given material (Table 10). The rigidity of the structure is clearly illustrated by the approximate constancy of the X-ray unit cell dimensions for different cationic forms of the same mineral (Table 11), the greatest change being seen in those members having the smallest channels,

TABLE 10

FREE DIAMETERS IN CERTAIN ZEOLITES[1]

Zeolite	Maximum diameter Å	Minimum diameter Å
Sodalite	∼ 6.6	∼ 2.2
Chabazite	∼ 7.3	∼ 3.2 ∼ 2.2
Linde sieves	∼ 11.8	∼ 4.2
Faujasite	∼ 12	∼ 9

TABLE 11

UNIT-CELL DIMENSIONS OF SOME CATIONIC FORMS
OF CERTAIN ZEOLITES[1]

Zeolite	Cationic composition	Unit cell dimensions Å		
		c	a	c/a
Ultramarine	75% Li^+, 25% Ag^+		8.7$_7$	
(cubic)	Ag^+		8.9$_7$	
	Na^+		9.0$_5$	
	80% K^+, 20% Ag^+		9.2$_5$	
Chabazite	Na^+	15.25	13.90	1.097
(hexagonal)	Ag^+	15.10	13.86	1.089
	Ca^{++}	15.00	13.85	1.083
	Ba^{++}	15.20	13.86	1.089
Faujasite	Na^+		24.8$_9$	
(cubic)	K^+		25.0$_3$	
	Ag^+		24.9$_1$	
	Tl^+		25.0$_6$	
	Ca^{++}		24.8$_7$	
	Sr^{++}		25.0$_1$	
	Ba^{++}		24.9$_8$	

e.g. ∼5% variation for ultramarine compared with ∼0.8% for chabazite and faujasite.

MOLECULAR SIEVE PROPERTIES OF THE ZEOLITES

The porous structure of the zeolites makes it possible to use them for the sorption of gases and vapours at suitable temperatures provided that the dimensions of the channels and cavities are suitable. Owing to the rigid structure and the ease with which the channel dimensions may be varied by varying the ionic form of the zeolite their specificity towards gaseous absorption may be varied almost at will[2]. Figs. 10 and 11 show the rates of diffusion of a number of gases into a given zeolite and of a single gas into a number of different cationic forms of the same material[3]; in these the uptake of gas is plotted as a function of (time)$^{\frac{1}{2}}$, since it is

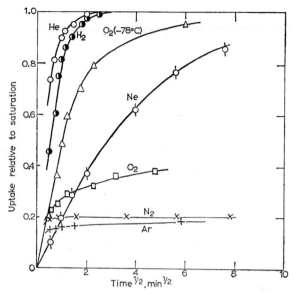

Fig. 10. Relative sorption rates for different gases on Ca mordenite at $-185°C$.[3] O_2 sorption is also shown at $-78°$ C for comparison. [Reproduced, with permission, from *Trans. Faraday Soc.*, 45 (1949) 362.]

found that initially the uptake follows a parabolic law (p. 66). The salient features which emerge are as follows:

(i) for a given cationic form of absorbent the uptake decreases as the atomic or molecular diameter of the gas is increased, and large molecules may be excluded altogether;

(ii) for a given gas the uptake decreases as the channel diameter is decreased by increasing the diameter of the cation present in the sorbent, or by introducing water molecules or anions into the channels.

Measurements of the heats of sorption of benzene and of *n*-hexane on various cationic forms of Linde Sieves A and X at temperatures from 260 ° to 482 °C illustrate[21] how the sorptive properties change markedly when sodium is replaced by other cations. On the Li^+, Na^+ and K^+ forms the heats are 16.0 and 12.0 kcal $\cdot$ mole^{-1} for benzene and *n*-hexane respectively, while the values for benzene sorption on bivalent cationic forms are 11.6 (Mg^{++}), 21.8 (Ca^{++}), 11.2 (Zn^{++}), 23.3 (Sr^{++}), 24.0 (Cd^{++}) and 10.0

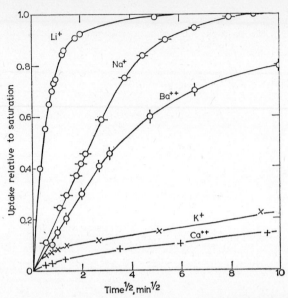

Fig. 11. Relative sorption rates for argon at $-78°$ C on mordenite in different cationic forms[3]. [Reproduced, with permission, from *Trans. Faraday Soc.*, 45 (1949) 367.]

(Ba^{++}). The high value for the cadmium form leads to much higher ratios of retention times for benzene/n-hexane and hexene-1/n-hexane mixtures, and suggests that this material would be useful in high-temperature gas-solid chromatography.

Three categories of molecular sieve have been distinguished by Barrer[2] according to the minimum diameters of the interstitial channels, although it is emphasized that the classification is not precise, since the sorptive properties of members having larger channels may be made to resemble those of zeolites having narrow channels by not removing the water completely from the channels of the former. By careful choice of the particular zeolite and of its cationic composition it is possible to effect a wide range of chromatographic separations, and the scope of the method may be extended appreciably by working at different temperatures, since two molecules which are sorbed at similar rates at one temperature may have quite different rates of uptake if the temperature is lowered. Since the sorptive power of zeolites is usually very much greater for polar molecules than for non-polar species, it is usually easy to effect a separation between these two types, and considerable use is made of zeolites as drying agents for gases. The development of the Linde molecular sieves (p. 55) in recent years has made it possible to use such processes on an industrial scale; as drying agents they are greatly superior to reagents such as activated alumina and silica gel, particularly where it is required to dry large volumes of gases at elevated temperatures with high efficiency. Two principal types are available commercially, Types 4A and 5A. The first has a channel diameter of 4 Å and will absorb a wide variety of polar molecules (H_2O, H_2S, SO_2, CO_2, NH_3), permanent gases (N_2, O_2, CH_4) at low temperatures, C_2 hydrocarbons and the lower alcohols. Type 5A has a channel diameter of 5 Å and will in addition absorb n-paraffins up to C_{14}, as well as n-olefines above C_3 and the higher n-alcohols, but will not absorb branched-chain paraffins and alcohols, or aromatic and other cyclic hydrocarbons. The molecular sieves may also be used to dry liquids, particularly if the molecules of the latter are unable to penetrate the structure, and they are readily regenerated after use by heating and purging with a gas such as nitrogen.

THE ZEOLITES AS IONIC SIEVES

Ionic sieve properties can arise in the zeolites either because channel diameters are too small to permit the passage of certain cations or because, when the cations concerned are above a certain size, the cavity dimensions are inadequate to accommodate the number of cations corresponding to the number of available exchange sites. In either case the zeolite tends to behave as a semi-permeable membrane, and very clean separations may be possible between certain pairs of ions.

In the first type of behaviour (Table 12) it is found that the number of ions which can undergo exchange increases as the zeolite

TABLE 12

RELATIVE UPTAKE OF MONOVALENT CATIONS BY DIFFERENT ZEOLITES[1]

Exchanger	Extent of exchange					
	Nil	Negligible	Slight	Medium	Considerable	Extensive
Ultramarine	Cs^+		NH_4^+, Rb^+		Li^+, Na^+, Tl^+	Na^+, Ag^+
Analcite	Cs^+		Li^+	Rb^+, H^+		Na^+, K^+, NH_4^+, Tl^+, Ag^+
Mordenite				Li^+	K^+, $MeNH_3^+$	H^+, Na^+, NH_4^+
Chabazite					Li^+, Cs^+, $MeNH_3^+$	H^+, Na^+, K^+, NH_4^+, Ag^+
Faujasite	NEt_4^+	NMe_4^+ $NHMe_3^+$			$NH_2Me_2^+$ NH_3Me^+	H^+, NH_4^+, Na^+ K^+, Rb^+, Cs^+, Tl^+, Ag^+

structure becomes more open, from the ultramarines to faujasite, until with the latter not only are the larger alkali metal cations accepted, but also large organic cations and bivalent metals, which undergo little exchange within the more compact structures. In faujasite the extent of exchange among the alkaline earths decreases in the order $Ba^{++} > Sr^{++} > Ca^{++} > Mg^{++}$, suggesting that the hydrated ions are involved, although in the more compact structures such as ultramarine the affinity towards the alkali metal cations indicates that in this case the unhydrated ions are concerned; it should be noted that of the zeolites listed in Table 12 ultramarine is the only one which is unhydrated (Table 9).

This type of ion-sieve behaviour makes it possible to carry out certain specific separations, e.g. analcite exchanges freely with rubidium ions (radius 1.48 Å) but not with caesium (1.63 Å)[4], while ultramarine exchanges with potassium (1.33 Å) but not caesium[5]. Even where it is possible on steric grounds for both ions to undergo exchange, a partial separation may be achieved by utilising the fact that the rates of exchange are dependent upon the ionic radii, e.g. the rates of replacement of alkali metal cations by silver ions in ultramarine decrease in the order $Li^+ > Na^+ > K^+$. The ion-sieve action of analcite towards caesium has been studied as a possible means of separating the latter from the other alkali metals[6] and it was found that at 100 °C sodium and caesium may be quantitatively separated on silver analcite, caesium-free sodium being incorporated into the crystal leaving a sodium-free caesium solution. Potassium may similarly be quantitatively removed from solution, but a little caesium accompanies it, since the incorporation of potassium into silver analcite results in a phase change from the cubic to the tetragonal form, and the latter can accommodate caesium; no phase change accompanies the replacement of silver by sodium, both unit cells being cubic, and therefore caesium is completely excluded in this case. Partial separation of rubidium and caesium is possible, and again there is some incorporation of caesium into the crystal, but in addition it is difficult in this case to remove rubidium quantitatively from solution. It is also possible to utilise this type of ion exclusion in order to prepare certain zeolites which are partially in the hydrogen form; normally these cannot be prepared by treatment of the zeolite with acid, since under these conditions the anionic framework is chemically unstable and breaks down with the precipitation of hydrated silica, leaving aluminium in solution. If, however, silver analcite is treated with an aqueous solution of the halide of a cation which is too large to enter the structure (*e.g.* CsCl, NMe_4Br) it is found that a precipitate of the silver halide is formed in the solution, which also becomes alkaline[6]; the overall reaction may be written

$$AgX + M^+ + Hal^- + H_2O \rightarrow Ag\ Hal \downarrow + M^+ + OH^- + HX$$

where X represents the analcite framework, M^+ the large cation and Hal the halogen. This behaviour has been observed for several zeolites (ultramarine, cancrinite, chabazite, faujasite) and up to 60% of the exchangeable cations have been replaced by hydrogen ion in suitable cases. In order for it to operate the solution must contain no cations which are capable of entering the lattice, and in addition the cation originally present in the exchanger should form an insoluble compound with the anion present in solution.

References p. 68

TABLE 13

Ion	Exchanging solution	Percentage replacement	Cubic cell edge Å
NH_4^+	2 N NH_4Cl	92%	24.9
NH_3Me^+	2 N NH_3MeCl	58%	24.9
$NH_2Me_2^+$	1 N NH_2Me_2Cl	37%	24.9
$NHMe_3^+$	2 N $NHMe_3Cl$	28%	24.9
NMe_4^+	1 N NMe_4Br	23%	25.0
NH_3Et^+	2 N NH_3EtCl	50%	24.9
NEt_4^+	1 N NEt_4Cl	No exchange	—

Even when the channel diameter is sufficiently great to admit cations, a volume sieve effect can arise when the ions are so large that the internal volume of the exchanger is insufficient to accommodate the number of cations corresponding to its capacity[7]. This is clearly seen in Table 13, which illustrates the extent to which sodium ions may be replaced by substituted alkylammonium ions from concentrated solutions for two exchangers having open structures, Linde sieves A and X (p. 55). Whereas exchange is more than 90% complete for ammonium ions, the extent decreases steadily as the size of the cation increases, even though only in the cases of NEt_4^+ for Linde Sieve X and of NMe_4^+ and NEt_4^+ for Linde Sieve A is there exclusion due to the channel diameter being too small. In the case of Linde Sieve X the number of NMe_4^+ ions which would fill the available free space in the unit cell may be calculated to be approximately 30, since this is the saturation uptake for neopentane, $C(CH_3)_4$, which is of similar size; the exchange capacity for sodium ions corresponds however to 82 cations per unit cell, and therefore not more than $\sim 40\%$ of the sites may be occupied by the larger cations. Since electroneutrality must be preserved, the actual number will of course be much lower, as seen in Table 13. A further limit to the extent of exchange is set by the fact that water molecules must also be displaced, since the organic cations are unhydrated, and this may have unfavourable consequences energetically.

SELECTIVITY IN THE ZEOLITE SERIES

When extreme effects due to ion sieve action are absent, the zeolites may still display marked selectivities towards certain ions due to differing thermodynamic affinities. The selectivity quotient K_B^A for pairs of ions A and B (for definition see p. 2) is given[8] for a number of cations in Table 14. The affinity varies rather unpredictably, and in some cases (Na^+–Rb^+ and Na^+–Tl^+ on chabazite) is strongly dependent on the cationic composition of the exchanger. Certain well-marked sequences are apparent on some exchangers, *e.g.*

Chabazite: $K^+ \gg Na^+$ at all compositions
$Tl^+ > K^+ > Ag^+ \sim Rb^+ > Na^+$ at equivalent loadings of both cations

Basic sodalite: $Ag^+ \gg Na^+ > Li^+ > K^+$

Although the reasons for these striking selectivity patterns are still not established, use may be made of them in a number of instances. Basic sodalite can be used under suitable conditions for the recovery of silver in quantitative analysis, while the mineral clinoptilolite (p. 62) may be employed to remove trace concentrations of caesium from solutions containing much higher concentrations of sodium, and has been tested as an absorbent for the treatment of

TABLE 14

SELECTIVITY QUOTIENTS K_B^A ON DIFFERENT ZEOLITES[8]

N_A	Basic sodalite			Chabazite			Ultra-marine	Basic cancrinite
B A Temp.	Na Li 85°	Na K 85°	Na Ag 25°	Na Ag 25°, 45°	K Ag 25°	Na Rb 85°	Na Li 75°	Na Li 25°, 85°, 110°
0.1	0.46	0.063	335	14	1.88	71.6	0.0038	13.8
0.3	0.47	0.064	335	13.0	1.27	29.2	0.0044	5.1
0.5	0.47	0.063	335	12.2	0.85	11.8	0.0053	1.9
0.7	0.47	—	335	11.4	0.57	4.7	—	0.7
0.9	—	—	335	10.6	0.38	1.9	—	0.3

References p. 68

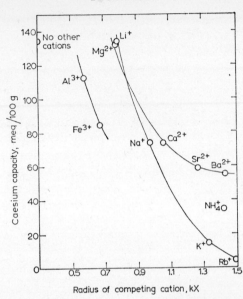

Fig. 12. Effect of competing cations on caesium capacity of Hector clinoptilolite[9]. Cs concentration 0.01 N. Total concentration 1.01 N. pH 3 (except
Al^{3+} and Fe^{3+}, pH 1.2). 25° C. Column contained 5 g of mineral, mesh size
0.25–1.0 mm. [Reproduced, with permission, from *Am. Mineralogist*, 45 (1960)
689.]

low-activity radioactive waste solutions[9]. A similar instance in
nature is found in the concentration of potassium relative to sodium
from sea-water by the mineral phillipsite, which occurs in deep-sea
sediments. The great selectivity of clinoptilolite towards caesium
is illustrated in Fig. 12.

A recent application of zeolite selectivity involves the use of a
synthetic ultramarine to separate the francium isotope ^{223}Fr from
its actinium parent and other activities[10]. The highly-charged
cations ^{227}Ac, ^{227}Th, ^{215}Po and ^{211}Pb are strongly absorbed, while
^{223}Fr, ^{207}Tl and ^{223}Ra pass through the column and may subsequently be separated from each other. In addition, ^{223}Fr formed
by α-decay of the ^{227}Ac retained on the column may be eluted
from the latter at intervals with 0.5 N ammonium chloride, thus
providing a source of pure francium.

THE LINDE MOLECULAR SIEVES—DOUBLE SIEVE ACTION

The Linde Molecular Sieves synthesised and studied by Breck[11] and by Barrer[12] furnish an interesting example of double sieve action arising from the presence of more than one size of channel in the structure. The principal members of this series are the sodium form (Linde Sieve 4A) and the calcium form (Linde Sieve 5A), which are available commercially. Analytical data and X-ray structural examination of the former show it to possess the formula $Na_{12}[12AlO_2 \cdot 12SiO_2] \cdot NaAlO_2 \cdot 29H_2O$, with a pseudo-cubic unit cell of side 12.273 ± 0.003 kX[13,14]. The structure is built up from AlO_4^{5-} and SiO_4^{4-} tetrahedra which are linked together to form rings comprising 4, 6 and 8 members, leading to three sizes of cage which are linked together by three sizes of channel as follows:

α-cage: 8-membered rings,
       channel diameter 4.2 ± 0.2 Å, cage diameter 11.4 Å.
β-cage: 6-membered rings,
       channel diameter 2.5 ± 0.2 Å, cage diameter 6.6 Å.
γ-cage: 4-membered rings,
       with dimensions too small to permit diffusion of ions.

X-ray data indicate that each unit cell contains one β-cage, which probably contains the $NaAlO_2$ grouping in the above formula, since

TABLE 15

EXTENT OF SUBSTITUTION OF ALKYLAMMONIUM IONS
ON LINDE SIEVE A[14]

Exchanging ion	Normality of solution	Exchange %	R_4N^+ ions per unit cell	H_2O molecules per unit cell
NH_3Me^+	8	77.7	10.10	12.8
NH_3Et^+	6	59.6	7.76	12.4
NH_3Pr^+	6	26.0	3.38	20.3
NH_3Bu^+	6	12.7	1.65	23.3
$NHMe_3^+$	5	14.2	1.84	27.6
NMe_4^+	6	0	—	—
NEt_4^+	6	0	—	—

References p. 68

this is not readily extracted; the dimensions of this cage approximate to those in the structure of sodalite. Extensive exchange was found to occur[14] with the ions Li+, K+, Ag+, Tl+, Ca++, Sr++, Mg++ and Pb++, while the ions NH_4+, Ba++, Zn++, Ni++ and Co++ caused breakdown of the structure when undergoing exchange; substituted ammonium ions also exchanged to the extent shown in Table 15. The unit cell constant varies slightly, from 12.273 kX for NaA to 12.285 for TlA, while the water content of the unit cell decreases as the cation radius is increased, from 28.6 molecules for NaA (radius 0.98 Å) to 22.6 for TlA (radius 1.49 Å). Chemical analysis of the exchanged forms shows that it is not always possible to displace the thirteenth sodium ion which is present in the β-cage, e.g. the extreme forms prepared by displacement of sodium by silver, thallous and calcium ions have the following formulae:

$$Ag_{12}[12AlO_2 \cdot 12SiO_2] \cdot AgAlO_2 \cdot nH_2O$$
$$Tl_{12}[12AlO_2 \cdot 12SiO_2] \cdot NaAlO_2 \cdot nH_2O$$
$$Ca_6[12AlO_2 \cdot 12SiO_2] \cdot NaAlO_2 \cdot nH_2O$$

In the case of the thallous form, complete replacement is prevented by steric considerations, but in the calcium form electrostatic forces are also involved, since the introduction of a bivalent cation into a singly-charged β-cage would necessitate the presence of an empty cage elsewhere in the structure; this would lead to charge separation, and would be energetically unfavourable[15].

Consideration of the limiting radii of exchangeable cations enables values to be obtained for the channel dimensions which are in good agreement with those deduced from X-ray data. For example, exchange is possible with ions up to $NHMe_3$+ ($r = 2.25$ Å), but not with NMe_4+ (2.4 Å), setting an upper limit to the channel diameter between 4.5 and 4.8 Å, compared with the measured value of 4.2 ± 0.2 Å. Similarly, complete replacement is possible with Ag+ (1.26 Å) but not with Tl+ (1.44 Å), leading to a value for the β-channel diameter between 2.5 and 2.9 Å, the measured value being 2.5 ± 0.2 Å. Linde Sieve 4A thus displays a double ion-sieve action; with other members of this structural series having Al:Si ratios differing from unity the number of cations per unit cell may be non-integral, and in this case incomplete exchange may result from deviations from the ideal composition rather than from a true ion-sieve mechanism. Table 15 also shows that for long-chain alkylammonium ions there may be a volume sieve effect if the ion can enter in a stretched configuration; since in principle more space can be made available by displacing water molecules which are associated with the sodium ions remaining in the cages, additional energy terms will be involved, leading to an increase in the activation energy for exchange.

A quantitative expression of double ion-sieve action has been given by measurements of a number of exchange isotherms on the sodium form Linde Sieve 4A[16]. These show that while the silver–sodium exchange proceeds to completion (Fig. 13) the thallous–sodium and thallous–silver exchanges involve only twelve of the thirteen cations present in each unit cell (Fig. 14). The isotherms are completely reversible, and the exchanger is found to be highly specific towards silver ions (*cf.* sodalite, p. 53). The sigmoid curve for the silver–sodium exchange has been analysed in terms of two

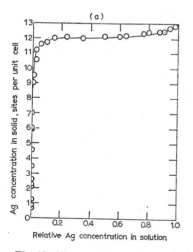
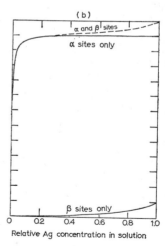

Fig. 13. Silver–sodium exchange isotherm on Linde Sieve 4A[16]; (a) measured isotherm, (b) analysis of curve in terms of two types of site. [Reproduced, with permission, from *Trans. Faraday Soc.*, 55 (1959) 130.]

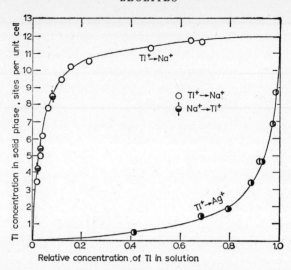

Fig. 14. Thallous–sodium and thallous–silver isotherms[16] on Linde Sieve 4A.

exchange processes involving α- and β-sites [Fig. 13(b)], while the partial exchange isotherms in Fig. 14 have been analysed in terms of exchange at α-sites only. The following values were obtained for the selectivity quotient K_A^B and the mass action constant $K' = \gamma_s K_A^B$, where γ_s is the ratio of solution activity coefficients:

Exchange	Site	K_A^B	$K' = \gamma_s K_A^B$
Tl → Na	α	25.9 ± 2.0	31.6 ± 2.4
Tl → Ag	α	$0.0465 \pm .0042$	$0.0723 \pm .0065$
Ag → Na	α	535 ± 12 (cf. 335 for basic sodalite)	464 ± 10
	β	0.136 ± 0.15	$0.118 \pm .012$

The existence of two types of exchange site in this system leads to sigmoid isotherms even though complete exchange is possible; other reasons for this phenomenon are discussed below.

EXCHANGE ISOTHERMS IN THE ZEOLITES

The rigid structures, absence of swelling and relatively small changes in water content between different cationic forms of the zeolites lead in many cases to considerable simplifications in the thermodynamics of exchange compared with the clays and with the organic ion-exchange resins, and in many cases ideal behaviour is approached. In the case of ideal solid phase behaviour the thermodynamic equilibrium constant is equal to the product of the selectivity quotient and the appropriate activity coefficient ratio in solution (p. 25). For exchange between two monovalent ions A^+ and B^+ a plot of log $[\bar{A}^+]$ $[B^+]$ *versus* log $[A^+]$ $[\bar{B}^+]$ will then be a straight line of unit slope with an intercept equal to the logarithm of the selectivity quotient. This behaviour has been observed in a small number of cases, *e.g.* Ag^+/Na^+ on chabazite[15] and Li^+/Na^+ on basic sodalite[8] (Fig. 15). If, however, the solid phase does not

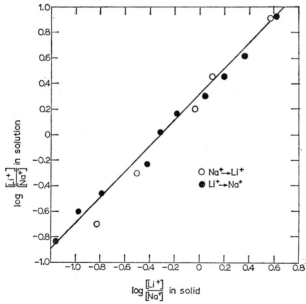

Fig. 15. Mass-action plot for lithium–sodium exchange[8] on basic sodalite at 85°C. [Reproduced, with permission, from *Proc. Roy. Soc.*, A236 (1956) 227.]

behave ideally, the selectivity quotient then becomes dependent upon the exchanger composition, and in this case the solid phase activity coefficients must be introduced into the expression for the thermodynamic constant as well as the solution activity coefficients. In practice however, the procedure is normally reversed, in that the thermodynamic constant is first derived by integration over the whole range of exchanger composition, after which the solid phase activity coefficients may be derived by a method such as that described by Gaines and Thomas (Ch. 2, ref. 8). In such cases the isotherms are frequently sigmoid in shape, even though there is only one type of site involved, as in the Li^+/Na^+ exchange on basic cancrinite[8] [Fig. 16 (a)]. These may be analysed by a method suggested by Kielland[17] in which the solid phase activity coefficients for the ions A^+ and B^+ are given by the expressions

$$\log \varGamma_A = CN_B{}^2 \text{ and } \log \varGamma_B = CN_A{}^2$$

where C is a constant and N_B and N_A are the mole fractions of the two ions in the exchanger, $i.e.$ $N_B = [\overline{B^+}]/\{[\overline{A^+}] + [\overline{B^+}]\}$ and $N_A = [\overline{A^+}]/\{[\overline{A^+}] + [\overline{B^+}]\}$. Since $N_A + N_B = 1$, the thermodynamic equilibrium constant is given by the expression

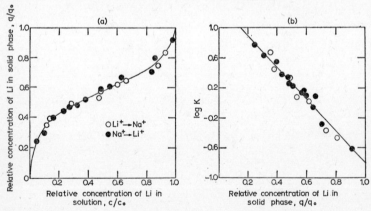

Fig. 16. Lithium–sodium exchange[8] on basic cancrinite at 85° C. (a) isotherm; (b) plotted in the form of Kielland's equation

$$\log K = \log \frac{m_B N_A}{m_A N_B} + C(1 - 2N_A)$$

[Reproduced, with permission, from $Proc.\ Roy\ Soc.$, A236 (1956) 227.]

$$\log K = \log \frac{[B^+]\,[\overline{A}^+]}{[\overline{B}^+]\,[A^+]} + \log \frac{\gamma_B}{\gamma_A} + \log \frac{\Gamma_A}{\Gamma_B}$$

$$= \log \frac{[B^+]\,[\overline{A}^+]}{[\overline{B}^+]\,[A^+]} + \log \frac{\gamma_B}{\gamma_A} + C(1 - 2N_A)$$

Since in dilute solutions containing two cations of the same valency γ_B/γ_A is approximately unity, a plot of

$$\log \frac{[B^+]\,[\overline{A}^+]}{[\overline{B}^+]\,[A^+]}$$

versus either N_A or N_B gives a straight line from which K may be calculated [Fig. 16 (b)].

The thermodynamic constant K may also be calculated in cases where the exchange is reversible by applying the same treatment as in the case of the clays with results such as those shown for chabazite in Table 16[15]. The main features which these data reveal are the small magnitudes of the free energy and heat of exchange, $\Delta G°$ and $\Delta H°$, and the affinity series $Na^+ < Ag^+$, $Rb^+ < K^+ <$ Tl^+. Table 16 also includes data reported recently[18] for the $Cs^+/$ Na^+ exchange on the mineral clinoptilolite, which possesses an even higher affinity for caesium than does montmorillonite (p. 28); the use of this mineral has been suggested for the removal of caesium

TABLE 16

THERMODYNAMIC DATA FOR EXCHANGE ON CHABAZITE AND CLINOPTILOLITE[15,18]

Exchanger	Exchange system	Temperature °C	K	$\Delta G°$ kcal/g ion, 25 °C
Chabazite	$Na^+ \rightleftharpoons Ag^+$	25–45	11.4	−1.44
	$Na^+ \rightleftharpoons K^+$	25	13.6	−1.53
	$Na^+ \rightleftharpoons Rb^+$	85	12.6	−1.50
	$Na^+ \rightleftharpoons Tl^+$	45	96.2	−2.90
	$K^+ \rightleftharpoons Ag^+$	25	0.8_6	+0.10
Clinoptilolite	$Cs^+ \rightleftharpoons Na^+$	50	23.3	−2.02
		75	13.2	−1.79

from low-activity wastes arising from nuclear processing plants. Clinoptilolite has the empirical formula

$$(Na_2O)_{0.70}(CaO)_{0.10}(K_2O)_{0.15}(MgO)_{0.05}Al_2O_3 \cdot 8.5–10.5SiO_2 \cdot 6–7H_2O$$

and its saturation capacity of 1.61 ± 0.01 meq/g is comparable to that of montmorillonite. Sigmoid isotherms are also observed in another class of inorganic ion exchanger, which is represented by zirconium phosphate and zirconium oxide (p. 125).

Recent measurements of heats of exchange and of exchange isotherms have thrown light on the energetics and mechanism of exchange on Linde Sieve 4A[22]. The sample chosen, the sodium form, contained a small amount of hydrogen ion as represented by the formula

$$HNa_{11}[12AlO_2 \cdot 12SiO_2] \cdot NaAlO_2 \cdot 27.6H_2O$$

(*cf.* p. 55). Treatment with lithium, potassium and calcium solutions produced complete conversions to

$$HLi_{11}X \cdot LiAlO_2 \cdot 26.3H_2O, \ HK_{11}X \cdot KAlO_2 \cdot 24.7H_2O$$
and
$$Ca_6X \cdot NaAlO_2 \cdot 30.7H_2O$$

respectively, but only partial conversion to the rubidium and caesium forms occurred

$$(HRb_{8.4}Na_{2.6}X \cdot NaAlO_2 \cdot 23.5H_2O$$
and
$$HCs_{5.4}Na_{5.6}X \cdot NaAlO_2 \cdot 21.8H_2O),$$

presumably for steric reasons. A simple calorimeter was used under non-isothermal conditions to measure heats of wetting and heats of equilibration of the different forms as well as heats of partial exchange as a function of exchanger composition. The heats of total exchange were then obtained from a summation of the heats of partial exchange from the two extreme cationic forms to a mixed form, except in the case of the rubidium and caesium forms, where extrapolation was necessary. By appropriate thermodynamic treatment the standard heats of partial exchange ΔH_q° may be obtained

TABLE 17

STANDARD THERMODYNAMIC FUNCTIONS FOR EXCHANGE
ON LINDE SIEVE 4A[22]

System	$\Delta H°$ kcal (g equiv)$^{-1}$	$\Delta G°$ kcal (g equiv)$^{-1}$	$T\Delta S°$ cal (g equiv)$^{-1}$	Kielland coefficient, C
NaA + Li$^+$ ⇌ LiA + Na$^+$	+2.26	+1.30	+960	−0.21
NaA + K$^+$ ⇌ KA + Na$^+$	−2.39	+0.14	−2530	−0.20$_5$
NaA + Rb$^+$ ⇌ RbA + Na$^+$	−2.55	+0.68	−3230	−0.70
NaA + Cs$^+$ ⇌ CsA + Na$^+$	−3.80	+1.98	−5780	−2.30
2 NaA + Ca^{++} ⇌ CaA$_2$ + 2 Na$^+$	+2.10	−0.14	+2240	—

as a function of composition, as well as the differential heats of
partial exchange $\partial(\Delta H_q°)/\partial q$. The standard free energies $\Delta G°$ were
obtained either from Kielland plots or from treatment of the ex-
change data by the method of Gaines and Thomas (Table 17).

The thermochemical data show that the Li$^+$/Na$^+$, Cs$^+$/Na$^+$ and
Ca^{++}/Na$^+$ exchanges are energetically quite heterogeneous (Fig.
17), the others much less so; in the first of these the stepped curve
suggests the presence of two types of site, with 4–5 and 8–9 cations
respectively, which agrees to some extent with X-ray data, although
the position of the sodium ions in the β-cages is not clear. The
heterogeneity is more complex in the cases of the Cs$^+$/Na$^+$ and
Ca^{++}/Na$^+$ systems, and may result in part from displacement of

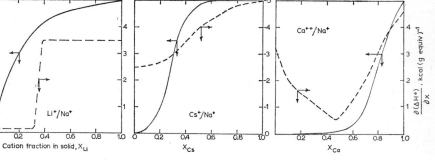

Fig. 17. Isotherms and differential heats of partial exchange on Linde Sieve
4A at 25°C as a function of solid composition[22]. [Reproduced, with permission,
from *Proc. Roy. Soc.*, A273 (1963) 180.]

cation positions when ions of greater size and charge are involved; changes in degree of hydration may also contribute. The exchange isotherms may be represented by linear Kielland plots, indicating continuous solid solubility, except in the case of the Ca^{++}/Na^+ exchange, where calculations of the solid phase activity coefficients show a maximum and minimum for Γ_{Na} and Γ_{Ca} respectively as a function of composition. Although all the isotherms show initially a greater affinity for the other ions relative to Na^+, only in the case of Ca^{++} is $\Delta G°$ negative, showing that the overall affinity favours Na^+ in the 1:1 exchanges studied (Table 17). $\Delta H°$ and $\Delta S°$ are of the same sign but opposite to $\Delta G°$ except for lithium, the displacement of a small univalent ion by a larger one always being accompanied by a decrease in $H°$ and $S°$. In all cases except lithium the sign of $\Delta G°$ is largely determined by the entropy term.

The relative affinity series $Na^+ > K^+ > Rb^+ > Li^+ > Cs^+$, which resembles that obtained by Russian workers[23] for a related exchanger, shows that the affinity decreases with increasing crystal radius of the cation, unlike the behaviour in the polystyrene sulphonic acid resins; although the signs of $\Delta H°$ and $T\Delta S°$ are the same in the two cases, the magnitudes are much greater in the zeolites, and this may be due to the greater changes in cation hydration during exchange in the latter. It is clear from the differing affinity series which are obtained with zeolites of different structures that the factors which influence exchange behaviour are extremely complex, and that further work which combines structural, thermochemical and thermodynamic investigations is necessary before these can be elucidated.

The isotherms for some of the more compact zeolitic structures such as analcite and basic cancrinite show anomalous behaviour which arises out of the limited solid solubility of the two end-members of the exchange, and this may be further complicated by marked hysteresis and lack of reversibility, as in the K^+/Rb^+ exchange on analcite[8] (Fig. 18). When potassium replaces rubidium and the potassium content of the analcite is sufficiently great, potassium-rich crystals tend to nucleate and grow on or in the rubidium-rich matrix; this introduces positive free energy terms

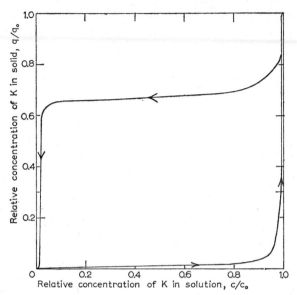

Fig. 18. Potassium–rubidium exchange on analcite at 95° C, showing hysteresis[8].

due to the contributions of strain and interfacial free energies, which in turn delay the spontaneous growth of potassium-rich crystals until the overall composition of the solid is well past that corresponding to thermodynamic equilibrium. A similar phenomenon will arise on the reverse cycle, so that exchange in either direction gives an isotherm with a hysteresis loop. Another consequence of this behaviour is that if crystals of analcite are treated with solutions which are saturated with respect to each of the exchanging ions the end point may depend upon the initial composition of the exchanger. A statistical treatment of such systems has been given by Barrer and Falconer[8].

THE KINETICS OF EXCHANGE ON ZEOLITES

The rate-controlling step in ion exchange is usually either diffusion of ions within the exchanger itself or within a thin film of solution surrounding the latter, depending upon the chemical and physical parameters of the system[19]. In the zeolites exchange is normally controlled by diffusion within the solid, and Barrer has shown[20] that for spherical particles the extent of exchange is governed initially by the expression

$$\frac{Q_t}{Q_\infty} = \frac{2A}{V} \sqrt{\frac{D^i t}{\pi}} = \frac{6}{r} \sqrt{\frac{D^i t}{\pi}} \qquad \text{for spherical particles,}$$

where Q_t and Q_∞ are the amounts of exchange at time t and at equilibrium respectively, A, V and r are the surface area, volume and radius of the exchanger particles. D^i is an effective (or apparent) diffusion coefficient which is related to the interdiffusion of the two exchanging ions. For simple interchange of cations A^{n+} and B^{n+} of the same valence, $D_A{}^i = D_B{}^i = D^i$ and D^i is independent of the exchanger composition. If, however, there is a statistical distribution of cations leading to space charges being set up by the two cations drifting independently of each other, then D^i is a function of the exchanger composition and its physical significance is less obvious. The apparent diffusion coefficient varies with temperature according to an expression of the Arrhenius type,

$$D^i = D_0{}^i \exp(-E/RT),$$

and values for a number of zeolites vary between 10^{-16} and 10^{-12} $cm^2 sec^{-1}$ (Table 18), while the activation energy for diffusion is of the order 10–30 kcal/g ion. Data for the exchange of a number of monovalent and bivalent cations on a sodium ultramarine[24] show that the reactivities decrease in the order

$$Ag^+ > Ni^{++} > Cu^{++} > Co^{++} > Mn^{++},$$

corresponding (except in the position of Ag^+) to an increasing ionic radius; in all cases except Ni^{++} the reactivity is governed largely by the magnitude of the activation energy, but for nickel the high value of the latter (24.6 kcal per g ion) is balanced by an unusually large pre-exponential factor, the complete expressions for the ionic diffusion coefficients being as follows:

Ag^+	$D^i = 6.96 \cdot 10^{-3} \exp(-17,700/RT)$
Cu^{++}	$0.245 \exp(-20,780/RT)$
Co^{++}	$1.06 \exp(-22,220/RT)$
Ni^{++}	$92 \exp(-24,600/RT)$
Mn^{++}	$3.5 \exp(-23,530/RT)$

The values of D^i are some 10^6 times lower than those for organic resins, and are reflected in the much lower rates of exchange; consequently zeolite exchange reactions are usually best carried out at temperatures of 100 °C or greater, and the low rates militate in general against the use of zeolites in cases where organic exchangers may be employed. The activation energies are comparable to those for the diffusion of ions in certain glasses, and are 2–4 times higher than those for exchange in organic resins, but the possible complexity of the reactions in the zeolites makes close comparison with other systems difficult.

TABLE 18

KINETIC DATA FOR EXCHANGE ON DIFFERENT
ZEOLITES AND ORGANIC RESINS[1]

Exchanger	Exchange	Temperature °C	$10^{14} D^i$ cm² sec⁻¹	E kcal/g ion
Basic cancrinite	$Na^+ \rightleftharpoons Li^+$	95	5.66	13.3
		25	0.05	
Analcite	$Na^+ \rightleftharpoons Tl^+$	110	45.2	14.9
		75	6.3	
Ultramarine	$Na^+ \rightleftharpoons Ag^+$	95	22.2	22.4
		60	0.89	
	$Ag^+ \rightleftharpoons Na^+$	75	1.25	21.9
		45	0.047	
	$Ag^+ \rightleftharpoons Li^+$	75	45.5	27.0
		45	10.0	
	$Ag^+ \rightleftharpoons K^+$	75	0.057	
Amberlite IR 1 cation resin	$Na^+ \rightleftharpoons Li^+$	30	3.0×10^8	
	$Na^+ \rightleftharpoons K^+$		3.5×10^8	
Phenol sulphonic acid cation resin	$NH_4^+ \rightleftharpoons NEt_4^+$	25	5.0×10^5	5.1
	$NH_4^+ \rightleftharpoons NMe_4^+$		2.4×10^6	—

REFERENCES

1 R. M. BARRER, *Proc. Chem. Soc.*, (1958) 99; *Chem. Ind.* (*London*), (1962 1258.

2 R. M. BARRER, *Quart. Rev.* (*London*), 3 (1949) 293.

3 R. M. BARRER, *Trans. Faraday Soc.*, 45 (1949) 358.

4 R. M. BARRER, J. W. BAYNHAM AND N. McCALLUM, *J. Chem. Soc.*, (1953) 4035.

5 R. M. BARRER AND J. S. RAITT, *J. Chem. Soc.*, (1954) 4641.

6 R. M. BARRER AND D. C. SAMMON, *J. Chem. Soc.*, (1956) 675.

7 R. M. BARRER AND J. W. SUTHERLAND, *Proc. Roy. Soc.* (*London*), A237 (1956) 439.

8 R. M. BARRER AND J. FALCONER, *Proc. Roy. Soc.* (*London*), A236 (1956) 227.

9 L. L. AMES, *Am. Mineralogist*, 45 (1960) 689.

10 W. HERR AND H. J. RIEDEL, *Radiochim. Acta*, 1 (1962) 32.

11 D. W. BRECK, W. G. EVERSOLE, R. M. MILTON, T. B. REED AND T. L. THOMAS, *J. Am. Chem. Soc.*, 78 (1956) 5963.

12 R. M. BARRER, J. W. BAYNHAM, F. W. BULTITUDE AND W. M. MEIER, *J. Chem. Soc.*, (1959) 195.

13 T. B. REED AND D. W. BRECK, *J. Am. Chem. Soc.*, 78 (1956) 5972.

14 R. M. BARRER AND W. M. MEIER, *Trans. Faraday Soc.*, 54 (1958) 1074.

15 *cf.* R. M. BARRER AND D. C. SAMMON, *J. Chem. Soc.*, (1955) 2838.

16 R. M. BARRER AND W. M. MEIER, *Trans. Faraday Soc.*, 55 (1959) 130.

17 J. KIELLAND, *J. Soc. Chem. Ind.*, 54 (1935) 232.

18 G. R. FRYSINGER, *Nature*, 194 (1962) 351.

19 See, for example, J. A. KITCHENER, *Ion-Exchange Resins*, Methuen, London, 1957, ch. 4.

20 R. M. BARRER AND L. HINDS, *J. Chem. Soc.* (1953) 1879; R. M. BARRER AND J. FALCONER, *Proc. Roy. Soc.*, (*London*), A236 (1956) 227.

21 P. F. EBERLY, *J. Phys. Chem.*, 66 (1962) 812.

22 R. M. BARRER, L. V. C. REES AND D. J. WARD, *Proc. Roy. Soc.* (*London*), A273 (1963) 180.

23 N. F. ERMOLENKO AND L. P. SHIRINSKAYA, *Russ. J. Phys. Chem.*, 36 (1962) 1317.

24 S. MAY, H. GOENVEC AND G. PINTE, *Report* CEA–1364, Saclay, 1959.

CHAPTER 4

Ion exchange in heteropolyacid salts

In the analytical determination of phosphorus as ammonium molybdophosphate it has long been known that if the precipitate is washed with potassium nitrate solution the ammonium ion is partially replaced by potassium, and that the washed precipitate may be converted to the original composition by treatment with ammonium nitrate solution[1]. Sodium ions also displace ammonium ion, but less efficiently than potassium, and the extent of exchange also depends upon the concentration of the solution used to wash the precipitate[2,3]. Thistlethwaite showed[4] that potassium did not replace more than two of the three ammonium ions in the formula $(NH_4)_3PMo_{12}O_{40}$, while the affinity of molybdophosphate towards the heavier alkali metal cations was found[5] to increase in the order, $K^+ < Rb^+ < Cs^+$.

The first systematic study of ion exchange on ammonium molybdophosphate was reported by Buchwald and Thistlethwaite[6], who treated the salt with 0.1–1 M solutions of Group I and Group II cations and of thallous ion, all in 0.08 M HNO_3. Complete mass balances were achieved for ammonium ion, while the number of equivalents of cation in the solid was found to remain constant and equal to three throughout all treatments. The results suggest that precipitated ammonium molybdophosphate does not possess the ideal formula given above, but is an acid salt with approximately 2.5 equivalents of ammonium ion and 0.5 of hydrogen ion. Both these ions may be replaced by other cations, but one ammonium ion per molecule appears to be more firmly held than the others. Extensive exchange was found for K^+, Rb^+, Cs^+ and Tl^+ ions, but only slight exchange for Li^+, Na^+ and the Group IIA cations. The relative affinities for the exchange of alkali metal cations on molybdophosphate are demonstrated quantitatively by the distribution coefficients measured by Smit[7] (Table 19).

TABLE 19

DISTRIBUTION COEFFICIENTS (K_d) AND THEORETICAL SEPARATION FACTORS (α) IN 0.1 M NH$_4$NO$_3$ SOLUTION

$$\alpha_{A^+,B^+} = K_d{}^{B^+}/K_d{}^{A^+}$$

Cation	Ammonium molybdophosphate		Dowex–50	
	K_d	α	K_d	α
Na$^+$	~0	—	26	
				1.7
K$^+$	3.4		46	
		68		1.1$_3$
Rb$^+$	230		52	
		260		1.1$_9$
Cs$^+$	6,000		62	

TABLE 20

DISTRIBUTION COEFFICIENTS FOR MONOVALENT CATIONS ON SOME HETEROPOLYACID SALTS[8]

Exchanger*	Method of preparation	K_d, ml · g^{-1}		
		Cs$^+$	Rb$^+$	K$^+$
AMP	Direct	5504 ± 50	192 ± 1	4 ± 1
	Via free acid	5566 ± 70	—	—
AMA	Direct	694 ± 4	125 ± 1	20 ± 1
	Via free acid	4155 ± 25	187 ± 1	5.5 ± 1
	Via Na salt	377 ± 4	—	33.0 ± 0.5
AWP	Via free acid	3280 ± 40	134	—
	Via Na salt	3495 ± 15	136	5.5 ± 1
QMP	Direct	1505 ± 5	—	—

Errors given indicate range of experimental data

* AMP: ammonium molybdophosphate
  AMA: ammonium molybdoarsenate
  AWP: ammonium tungstophosphate
  QMP: quinoline molybdophosphate

The differences between the behaviour of successive cations are indicated by the values of the theoretical separation factor α, which is equal to the ratio of the respective distribution coefficients for a given pair of ions. These values are seen to be very much greater than those for an organic exchanger such as Dowex–50, and in confirmation of this fact a highly efficient separation of the alkali metals in tracer concentrations in 0.1 N NH_4NO_3 solution was obtained on a bed of 5 mm diameter and depth 1.6 mm (Fig. 19). In a more detailed study[8] several 12-heteropolyacid salts were prepared and batch distribution coefficients measured for the alkali metal cations, Ag^+ and Tl^+ ions at pH 2.0, with the results shown in Table 20. The exchangers studied included ammonium molybdophosphate, molybdoarsenate, molybdosilicate, tungstophosphate, tungstoarsenate, tungstosilicate and oxine molybdophosphate. The results of this work may be summarized as follows:

(i) Under given conditions the uptake increases as the radius

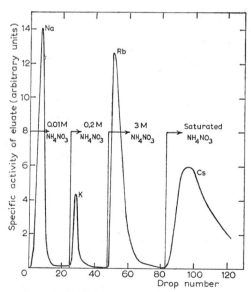

Fig. 19. Separation of alkali metals at tracer concentrations on a bed of ammonium molybdophosphate[7]. Diameter 5 mm, depth 1.6 mm. [Reproduced, with permission, from *Nature*, 181 (1958) 1530.]

of the unhydrated cation increases, as in the strongly acid organic exchangers.

(*ii*) Tl+ and Ag+ ions are held more strongly than alkali metal cations of similar size, possibly indicating some degree of covalency in the bonding.

(*iii*) Theoretical separation factors between adjacent elements in this series are more than ten times greater than those for Dowex–50.

(*iv*) The distribution coefficients are almost independent of pH between 1.1 and 4.5.

(*v*) Multivalent cations showed negligible exchange in acid solution, but are strongly absorbed from neutral solutions. While yttrium and cerium appear to be absorbed as the trivalent ions, ruthenium, zirconium, and niobium are apparently absorbed as complex species[23].

THE ION-EXCHANGE PROPERTIES OF THE HETEROPOLY-ACIDS IN RELATION TO THEIR STRUCTURE

The parent acids of the compounds considered in this chapter belong to the class of 12-heteropolyacids, having the general formula $H_3XY_{12}O_{40} \cdot nH_2O$, where X may be one of several elements including phosphorus, arsenic and silicon, and Y a different element such as molybdenum, tungsten and vanadium. X-ray studies of ammonium tungstophosphate[9] reveal a structure (Fig. 20) in which a PO_4 tetrahedron is surrounded by 12 linked WO_6 octahedra to form an approximately spherical anion by sharing oxygen atoms in a manner resembling the aluminosilicate structures of the zeolites (p. 43). The crystal lattice contains many such spheres, with cations and water molecules situated in the cavities between them. Both cations and water molecules are free to move within these cavities if considerations of size permit, thus permitting exchange of cations between the crystal and external solutions; in this respect the exchangers bear a strong resemblance to the zeolites. Ammonium ions, the large monovalent cations (K+, Rb+, Cs+, Tl+, Ag+, Hg_2^{2+}) and organic bases such as quinoline are large enough to pack stably into the structure and lower the lattice

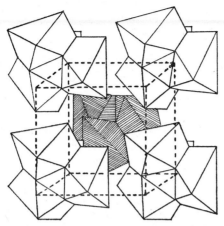

Fig. 20. Cubic unit cell of the tungstophosphate anion in the heavy alkali metal tungstophosphates[9]. Each unit cell contains two $(PW_{12}O_{40})^{3-}$ polyhedra formed by sharing edges between WO_6 octahedra located tetrahedrally about a central P atom. In the caesium salt Cs+ ions occupy positions at the centres of faces and in the middle of the edges of the cube. [Reproduced, with permission, from *J. Chem. Soc.* (1935) 575.]

energy sufficiently to form an insoluble crystal. Salts containing other alkali metal cations are much more soluble and are unsuitable for exchange purposes[10].

Although similar structural considerations presumably apply throughout the 12-heteropolyacid series, differences in behaviour have been observed between individual members which are as yet unexplained. Thus, although the ion-exchange behaviour of ammonium molybdophosphate is found to be the same whether it is prepared by direct precipitation of the salt from mixed molybdate and phosphate solutions or by adding NH_4NO_3 to the free acid, the tungstophosphate and molybdoarsenate show large variations in appearance and in values of K_d for various cations when prepared in different ways. X-ray powder photographs show the presence in these two salts of three different structures in varying proportions, only one of these structures being capable of undergoing exchange; all preparations of the molybdophosphate contain this component, while some preparations of the other salts do not.

COLUMN SEPARATION OF THE ALKALI METALS
ON AMMONIUM MOLYBDOPHOSPHATE[11]

Ammonium molybdophosphate as normally prepared is micro-crystalline (mesh size < 200 B.S.S.), and larger crystals normally break down readily in aqueous suspensions. Thus, although suitable for column separations on a micro-scale[7], a suitable support is required if the material is to be used for laboratory-scale work or plant operation. Smit has shown that a 1:1 mixture with Gooch asbestos may be used for the separation of macro-quantities of the alkali metals as shown in Figs. 21 and 22. The exchanger–asbestos mixture enables suitable flow-rates to be attained for a reasonable pressure-drop, and shows no tendency to separate on continued operation of the column; as in the case of clay–asbestos columns (p. 21) the asbestos contributes negligibly to the overall exchange capacity. The successful separation of the alkali metals on a tracer scale is repeated when macro-amounts are involved, and since the lower members form relatively soluble salts and thus are not appreciably absorbed by the exchanger it is possible to

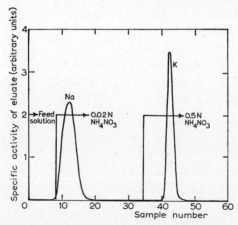

Fig. 21. Separation of sodium (104 mg) from potassium (1.02 mg) on ammonium molybdophosphate[8]. Column 0.81 cm^2 × 6.8 cm containing 1.48 g AMP + 0.74 g asbestos. [Reproduced, with permission, from *J. Inorg. Nucl. Chem.*, 12 (1959) 104.]

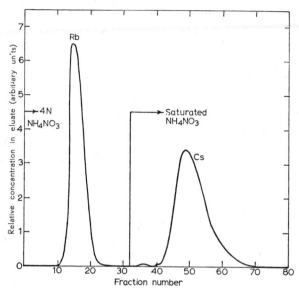

Fig. 22. Separation of rubidium (12.3 mg) and caesium (13.5 mg) on ammonium molybdophosphate[8]. Column 1.54 cm^2 × 8.9 cm containing 50:50 wt.% AMP + asbestos. [Reproduced, with permission, from *J. Inorg. Nucl. Chem.*, 12 (1959) 104.]

separate tracer quantities of the heavier alkali metals from much larger quantities of the lighter members, which would considerably overload the column if they were absorbed; similar considerations apply to the separation of the heavy alkali metals from multivalent cations in acid solution, where the latter are negligibly absorbed. The very high selectivity towards caesium enables the latter to be quantitatively removed from 20 litres of sea-water on a bed containing only 2 g of molybdophosphate–asbestos mixture, despite the very high ratio of sodium and potassium to caesium in the solution. Molybdophosphate columns may also be used for the separation of fall-out caesium from rain-, river- or sea-water[12]. In the alkali metal separations fairly symmetrical, sharp breakthrough curves are obtained at linear flow-rates of 1 cm/min.

Smit has recently described[24] a method of preparing coarse crystals of ammonium molybdophosphate which do not break down when repeatedly recycled in exchange systems. When coarse molybdophosphoric acid crystals are immersed in fairly concentrated solutions (4–10 M) of ammonium nitrate, replacement of hydrogen ions by ammonium ions to form the insoluble ammonium salt is accompanied by loss of water and an irreversible phase transition. The final product has a similar particle size distribution to the starting material, and appears to consist of coarse, stable agglomerates of smaller particles which retain approximately the regular shapes of the original crystals; the finer particles within the agglomerates are about 1–2 μ in diameter, while the overall particle size may be in excess of 40 B.S.S. mesh. The particles are physically stable over several cycles of absorption and elution if kept in contact with an electrolyte solution, but break down if allowed to dry out. By virtue of their structure, exchange is much more rapid than would be expected from consideration of their gross particle size alone, as diffusion will be relatively rapid and will be controlled ultimately by the size of the finer material (*cf.* p. 130). By using this material instead of asbestos–exchanger mixtures higher bed density and volume capacity are achieved, without the disadvantages attendant upon compaction of the bed when asbestos is used.

Since ammonium and caesium molybdophosphates are isomorphous the three ammonium ions would be expected to be equivalent and all exchangeable: the theoretical exchange capacity calculated from the formula $(NH_4)_3PMo_{12}O_{40} \cdot 2H_2O$ would then be 1.57 meq/g. Analysis of saturated columns from caesium and rubidium breakthrough experiments showed that in fact only $\sim 60\%$ exchange had occurred in the former instance and $\sim 80\%$ in the latter, confirming the difficulty which earlier investigators had experienced in attempting to completely displace the ammonium ions. Although this phenomenon still lacks explanation, it may be due to the larger cations partially blocking the channels, thus reducing cation mobility and inhibiting further exchange.

THE SEPARATION OF CAESIUM FROM FISSION PRODUCT WASTE SOLUTIONS

The high selectivity shown by the heteropolyacid salts towards caesium, even in acid solution, and the general stability of inorganic ion exchangers towards ionizing radiation, suggest that these might be effectively used for the recovery of caesium from the waste solutions resulting from the processing of irradiated nuclear fuels[13]. In a method developed in the U.S.A. for the decontamination of waste solutions[14] ammonium molybdophosphate was precipitated *in situ* on silica gel for use in columns. The product contained only 23% of the exchanger by weight or 10% by volume and was thus of inferior capacity compared with an exchanger–asbestos mixture or a coarse material. Furthermore, ammonium molybdophosphate was released steadily from the column when the acid feed solution was passed through the latter (32% after 100 column volumes of 0.1 N HNO$_3$), and the measured capacity of 0.25 meq/g represents a balance between caesium uptake and the loss of material from the column.

Greater success has been achieved in experiments with molybdophosphate–asbestos columns or with coarse molybdophosphate crystals[15], without experiencing loss of exchanger from the columns. With simulated fission-product waste solutions it has been shown that caesium is selectively absorbed at acidities up to 3 N in nitric acid, the maximum capacity of 0.70 meq/g corresponding to replacement of 1.4 ammonium ions per molecule of exchanger. If, after the absorption stage, the column is washed with dilute acid ($\sim$ 1 N), all other fission products except rubidium and zirconium-niobium may be removed; the latter may be removed by complexing elution with oxalic acid before recovery of caesium and rubidium. Owing to the high selectivity of the exchanger for these ions their elution is difficult unless concentrated solutions are used, and this would pose a fresh problem in the separation of caesium from a large excess of the eluting cation. The most promising solution involves dissolving the column in alkali to give a solution in which the ratio of caesium to the other alkali metal cation is sufficiently high to permit separation either by solvent extraction or by a further ion-exchange treatment. It has been suggested that use should be made at this stage of the high selectivity for caesium relative to sodium of another inorganic ion exchanger, zirconium phosphate (p. 107). After dissolution of the molybdo-phosphate column in NaOH the acidity of the solution would be adjusted to pH $\sim$ 4 and passed through a column of zirconium phosphate to absorb caesium, rubidium and sodium; sodium would then be eluted with dilute acid ($\sim$ 0.1 N) and caesium, together with rubidium, with $\sim$ 3 N acid. This two-stage process combines the advantages of the greater selectivity of molybdophosphate with the greater ease of elution from zirconium phosphate; it has however, yet to be tested on a large scale with actual waste solutions.

ABSORPTION AND SEPARATIONS INVOLVING POLYVALENT CATIONS[25]

As noted above, bivalent and trivalent cations are poorly absorbed from acid solutions but appreciably at pH 2–5; in the latter instance the system must be buffered to pH 4–5 with sodium acetate if macro-amounts are to be absorbed successfully. The alkaline earths may then be eluted with ammonium salt solutions and trivalent cations with an acid eluant, and simple group separations are possible as follows:

(i) Sr^{++}–Y^{+++} in tracer amounts: after absorption from neutral solution strontium may be eluted with 0.1 N NH_4NO_3 + 0.1 N HNO_3 and yttrium with 1 N NH_4NO_3 + 1 N HNO_3.

(ii) Sr^{++}–Y^{+++} in macro-quantities: if absorbed from an unbuffered solution separation is incomplete, but if the solution is buffered before absorption separation on elution proceeds as before.

(iii) Cd^{++}–In^{+++}: after absorption at pH 4 cadmium may be eluted with $N/8$ NH_4NO_3 and indium with 1 N NH_4NO_3 + 1 N HNO_3.

Detailed examination of the behaviour of polyvalent cations on ammonium molybdophosphate reveals interesting complexities in the exchange mechanism. Equilibrium determinations of K_d show that while the Sr^{++}/H^+ system obeys the mass action law (p. 3) the uptake of Y^{+++} increases to a maximum at pH 3.5 and decreases again to zero at pH 4 (*cf.* ammonium tungstophosphate, p. 80), in apparent contradiction to the behaviour noted above. The absorption of both Sr^{++} and Y^{+++} in column experiments from solutions buffered at pH 4–5 is apparently due to the fact that equilibrium is not attained at such short contact times, since the initial uptake from fresh solutions at pH 4.5 is high. On standing at this pH some breakdown of the exchanger occurs, with release of 11-molybdophosphate anions to the solution; presumably complexing elution of yttrium takes place simultaneously, since it was found that after standing fresh exchanger in contact with a solution at pH 4.5 no absorption of freshly-added yttrium occurred unless the exchanger was first transferred to a fresh solution. It is conceivable that the very strong initial absorption of yttrium on a fresh exchanger buffered at pH 4.5 may also be due to complexing within the solid. Conditions for uptake and elution are clearly different, since although absorption of Y^{+++} is poor below pH 3.5 it is necessary to use at least 0.5 N acid to elute it again, suggesting that once it is absorbed the ion can migrate to a less accessible site, or alternatively that strong bonding forces are involved. Consequently it is impossible to separate the trivalent ions chromatographically, since they are not re-absorbed from solution at the pH which is necessary for elution.

MISCELLANEOUS STUDIES ON HETEROPOLYACID SALTS

Although the bulk of the work in this field has been concentrated on ammonium molybdophosphate, particularly as regards the separation of the alkali metals, several other systems have been examined in less detail.

A comparison of potassium, rubidium and caesium molybdophosphates for the removal of traces of caesium, strontium and yttrium from neutral solutions showed that neither was superior to the ammonium salt, while the alkylammonium molybdophosphates were distinctly inferior[16]. Caesium, strontium and yttrium may be absorbed together from neutral solution and separated by first eluting strontium with 0.1 M nitric acid, followed by yttrium with 2 M acid, after which the exchanger may be dissolved in dilute ammonia to recover caesium. In this connection it is interesting to note that while ammonium molybdophosphate is appreciably soluble in 2 M nitric acid (179 · 10^{-6} moles · 1^{-1}), the solubility is greatly reduced in the presence of dissolved salts (1.3 · 10^{-6} M · 1^{-1} for 1.4 · 10^{-3} M $LiNO_3$, < 1 · 10^{-6} for 1.4 · 10^{-3} M $CsNO_3$).

Ammonium tungstophosphate has been used for the separation of rubidium and caesium[17] and of caesium, strontium and yttrium[18]. Comparison of caesium sorption on ammonium molybdo- and tungstophosphates[19] shows that the former exchanger is less stable in acid solution, although the caesium capacity per mole of exchanger is greater for the latter. The distribution coefficients for strontium and yttrium on ammonium tungstophosphate exhibit

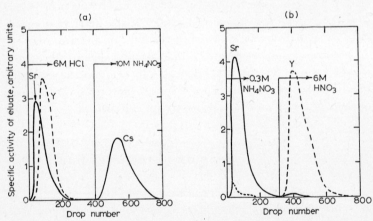

Fig. 23. Separation of caesium, strontium and yttrium in tracer amounts on ammonium tungstophosphate[18]. (a) Separation of caesium from strontium and yttrium. (b) Separation of strontium from yttrium; 0.2 g AWP + 0.2 g asbestos. [Reproduced, with permission, from *J. Inorg. Nucl. Chem.*, 22 (1961) 247.]

maxima at pH $\sim$ 3 and pH $\sim$ 1 respectively, the maximum uptake per mole of exchanger being 0.18 moles of strontium compared with 1.8 moles of caesium. After absorption of these ions. strontium and yttrium may be separated by elution with a neutral salt, and acid elution separates caesium from the other ions (Fig. 23). An efficient separation of caesium from rubidium and potassium by dilute acid elution from thallous tungstophosphate has also been reported[20]. Ammonium molybdotungstophosphate has also been shown to separate rubidium and caesium efficiently[26], the distribution coefficients decreasing as the ratio Mo:W was decreased from 2:1 to 1:2. Rubidium was eluted with 1 M NH_4NO_3 and caesium with 10 M NH_4NO_3.

CHROMATOGRAPHY ON PAPER IMPREGNATED WITH AMMONIUM MOLYBDOPHOSPHATE

The high selectivity of certain inorganic ion exchangers has been applied to paper chromatography by the use of papers impregnated with a suitable material[21] (see also p. 119). With ammonium molybdophosphate the alkali metals may first be separated into three groups (Cs + Rb; K; Na + Li) by developing with a solution of 0.1 N ammonium nitrate + 0.2 N nitric acid; after the paper is cut into three sections corresponding to these groups, caesium and rubidium are separated on the first by developing with 0.2 N nitric acid + 3.5 N ammonium nitrate, sodium and lithium on the third by developing with 95% ethanol. Certain of the natural radioelements have also been separated in this way either by paper chromatography or by direct filtration through impreg-

TABLE 21

DISTRIBUTION COEFFICIENTS FOR SOME MONOVALENT CATIONS ON AMMONIUM MOLYBDOPHOSPHATE FROM 0.1 M NH_4NO_3[22]

Ion	Na+	K+	Rb+	Cs+	Fr+	Ag+	Tl+
K_d	0	4	190	5500	?	26	4300

nated paper[22]. From Table 21 it will be seen that the distribution coefficients are very high for caesium and thallous ions from 0.1 M ammonium nitrate solution at pH 2, and the trend shown in the alkali metal series suggests that the value for francium will be very high indeed. These facts have been utilized in the separation of ThC″ (^{208}Tl) from ThB (^{212}Pb) and ThC (^{212}Bi) by developing on paper with 6 M nitric acid, the separation factor being 250, and of AcK (^{223}Fr) + AcC″ (^{207}Tl) from ^{227}Ac and its daughter products, again by development with 6 M nitric acid; in the latter case the separation factor increases from $2.2 \cdot 10^2$ to $2 \cdot 10^3$ as the acid concentration is increased from 1 to 6 M.

REFERENCES

1 G. P. BAXTER AND R. C. GRIFFIN, Am. Chem. J., 34 (1905) 204.
2 H. TERLET AND A. BRIAU, Ann. Fals. Fraudes, 28 (1935) 546.
3 L. GISIGER, Z. Anal. Chem., 115 (1938) 15.
4 W. P. THISTLETHWAITE, Analyst, 72 (1947) 531.
5 D. MEIER AND W. D. TREADWELL, Helv. Chim. Acta, 34 (1951) 155.
6 H. BUCHWALD AND W. P. THISTLETHWAITE, J. Inorg. Nucl. Chem., 5 (1958) 341.
7 J. VAN R. SMIT, Nature, 181 (1958) 1530.
8 J. VAN R. SMIT, J. J. JACOBS AND W. ROBB, J. Inorg. Nucl. Chem., 12 (1959) 95.
9 J. F. KEGGIN, Proc. Roy. Soc. (London), A144 (1934) 75; J. W. ILLINGWORTH AND J. F. KEGGIN, J. Chem. Soc., (1935) 575.
10 T. V. HEALY AND B. L. DAVIS, U.K.A.E.A. Reports AERE–C/R 2528 (1958); 2621 (1959); T. V. HEALY AND G. INGHAM, C/R 2594 (1958); T. V. HEALY, B. L. DAVIS AND G. INGHAM, C/R 2577 (1958).
11 J. VAN R. SMIT, W. ROBB AND J. J. JACOBS, J. Inorg. Nucl. Chem., 12 (1959) 104.
12 J. VAN R. SMIT, W. ROBB AND J. J. JACOBS, Nucleonics, 17 (9) (1959) 116.
13 For a general discussion, see C. B. AMPHLETT, Treatment and Disposal of Radioactive Wastes, Pergamon, Oxford, 1961, pp. 29–49.
14 M. W. WILDING, U.S. reports IDO–14540 (1960); IDO–14544 (1961); R. L. HICKOK, U.S. report TID–7613 (1960) p. 500.
15 J. VAN R. SMIT AND F. W. PUMMERY, U.K.A.E.A. reports AERE–R 3884 (1961), 4006 (1962), 4039 (1962); J. VAN R. SMIT, J. J. JACOBS AND F. W. PUMMERY, AERE–R 4245; H.M. Stationery Office, London, 1963.
16 R. W. C. BROADBANK, S. DHABANANDANA AND R. D. HARDING, J. Inorg. Nucl. Chem., 23 (1961) 311.
17 V. KOURZHIM et al., Dokl. Akad. Nauk SSSR, 140 (1961) 832.

18 J. Krtil, *J. Inorg. Nucl. Chem.*, 22 (1961) 247.
19 J. Krtil and V. Kouřím, *J. Inorg. Nucl. Chem.*, 12 (1960) 367, 370; 24 (1962) 1139.
20 H. L. Caron and T. T. Sugihara, *Anal. Chem.*, 34 (1962) 1082.
21 G. Alberti and G. Grassini, *J. Chromatog.*, 4 (1960) 423.
22 H. J. Schroeder, *Radiochim. Acta*, 1 (1962) 27.
23 J. Krtil and J. Zemanová, *J. Inorg. Nucl. Chem.*, 25 (1963) 1069.
24 J. van R. Smit, *U.K.A.E.A. report AERE*–R 3700 (1963).
25 J. van R. Smit and W. Robb, *J. Inorg. Nucl. Chem.*, 26 (1964) 509.
26 J. Krtil and I. Křivý, *J. Inorg. Nucl. Chem.*, 25 (1963) 1191.

CHAPTER 5

Hydrous oxides and insoluble salts

The fact that many insoluble oxides absorb cations or anions when suspended in aqueous solutions frequently proves embarrassing in analytical separations, since the removal of the impurity ions may be extremely difficult to achieve. The phenomenon has at various times been ascribed to a variety of causes, but its study as a branch of ion-exchange chemistry may be said to date from the discovery[1] in 1943 that the insoluble compound zirconium phosphate may be used to separate uranium and plutonium from fission products. Since that date interest in ion exchangers of this type has spread to a number of countries, and has been greatly stimulated by their stability towards ionizing radiation, high temperatures and most chemical reagents. Particular attention has been paid to them by countries with programmes in the nuclear energy field, in relation to chemical processing problems and to the treatment of contaminated moderator or cooling water in reactors working at high temperatures and pressures.

A large number of compounds has been studied, some more extensively than others; the account which follows will first describe the properties of hydrous oxides and of zirconium phosphate, to which most attention has been given. Other types will then be reviewed, after which various topics common to the series as a whole will be discussed.

THE HYDROUS OXIDES[2]

A wide range of observations on ion sorption by hydrous oxides can be interpreted on the basis of reversible ion-exchange equilibria, although it is not always clear from the early work whether sorption involves the bulk of the solid or only the surface; although this can be simply resolved by measuring the saturation capacity per unit mass as a function of surface area, such measurements were rarely carried out. Freshly-precipitated trivalent metal oxides are very effective in this respect, *e.g.* hydrous ferric oxide and ferric hydroxide readily absorb alkaline earth cations according to the law of mass action[3], other bivalent cations[4] being absorbed above pH 7. There is evidence to suggest that while the alkali metals and alkaline earths are absorbed on the surface and are readily eluted, more highly-charged cations (Ce^{+++}, Y^{+++}, Pm^{+++}, Ru^{++++}) are sorbed in bulk and eluted only with difficulty[5]. How far this is due to exchange is doubtful, since such ions would be coprecipitated on the oxide. Amphoteric oxides such as hydrous alumina may absorb either cations or anions depending upon the pH of the solution, and this has been ascribed to the following equilibria[6]:

$$Al(OH)_2{}^+ + OH^- \leftrightarrows Al(OH)_3 \rightleftharpoons AlO(OH)_2{}^- + H^+$$

The use of Al_2O_3 for chromatographic separations is of course well known[7], but this appears to be largely a surface phenomenon, since freshly-prepared material with a large surface area is very active, while aged oxide which has undergone recrystallization loses both surface area and chromatographic activity. By using Al_2O_3 and adjusting the solution pH to take advantage of its amphoteric properties it has proved possible to separate carrier-free isotopes such as ^{18}F, [99]Mo, ^{99m}Tc, [132]I and [132]Te, all of which exist in anionic forms in solution[8]. Molybdate and tungstate have also been separated after absorption at pH 1 on alumina which has been fired at 1000 °C and then digested with 2 N HCl; the former is eluted with 4 N HCl and the latter with 8 N acid[9]. Zinc oxide also appears to show amphoteric exchange properties; acid–base titrations show[10] that both hydrogen and hydroxyl ions can be absorbed, although[94] the pH range over which exchange is possible is limited to 6.5–9.5.

Zeta-potential measurements as a function of pH on thoria and on synthetic magnetite[88] have also been interpreted in terms of amphoteric behaviour of surface hydroxyl groups, and have been used to derive ion adsorption isotherms. In the case of thoria two modes of dissociation were postulated with $pK_H = 2.9$ and $pK_{OH} = 11.1$; as in the case of bulk ion exchange by thoria (p. 91), anion exchange predominates on the surface also. The magnetite surface is more feebly basic, with $pK_{OH} = 4.4$, the affinity towards different anions increasing in the order

$$Cl^- \ll SO_4^{--} < HCO_3^- < CrO_4^{--} < HPO_4^{--} < Fe(CN)_6^{4-}.$$

The amphoteric behaviour of magnetite towards ion absorption from neutral solution has also been demonstrated directly[90], and its relationship to the hydroxyl content is shown by the fact that dry preparations are much less effective than those prepared by wet methods. Crystalline ferric acid (α-haematite) also shows[89] evidence of amphoteric surface behaviour when titrated against acidic or basic solutions, with an isoelectric point at pH 8.5.

The scavenging properties of freshly-precipitated manganese dioxide towards fission-products in solution have long been utilised for removal of the latter, and several workers have shown[11-13] that hydrogen ions are released when non-stoichiometric γ-MnO$_2$ is suspended in aqueous salt solutions. Manganites have been shown to possess ion-exchange properties[14], and MnO$_2$ was found to undergo surface exchange to a small extent with manganous ions in solution[15]. β-MnO$_2$ displays a much smaller capacity than the γ-oxide, exchanging $\sim 10^{-2}$ milliequivalents of H$^+$ ion for an equivalent amount of Zn^{2+} when suspended in a solution of a zinc salt[13]; a similar capacity was measured for a β-MnO$_2$ of composition MnO$_{1.92}$ immersed in a manganous salt solution[16]. The irreproducible behaviour of the MnO$_2$ electrode[11] and the drift in potential which occurs when the electrode is initially immersed in a solution or when the solution concentration is changed[17] may also be attributed to ion-exchange reactions taking place between the electrode and the solution. β-MnO$_2$, containing an excess of manganous ions and with compositions ranging from MnO$_{1.992}$ to MnO$_{1.997}$, slowly absorbed hydrogen ions from acid solutions up to 0.1 N with release of an equivalent quantity of Mn^{2+} ions. The capacity varied from 0.05 to 0.2 meq/g, depending upon the particular sample chosen, its particle size and the degree of shaking. Exchange was found to be reversible, faster at 100 °C than at room temperature, but was less on samples which had been heated in oxygen for 48 h at 400 °C, a treatment which oxidizes Mn^{2+} and improves the stoichiometry. Titration with acid at a total chloride concentration of 0.1 M suggests that the oxide contains two functional groups with pK values of 3.8 and 5.2. The surface area of the oxide (< 0.1 m^2/g) is too small for the exchange to be confined to the surface, while the kinetics of the uptake suggest that a fast initial surface exchange is followed by slower diffusion into the bulk of the material. A better correlation between surface area and capacity is obtained for γ-MnO_2, which possesses a more open structure[13]. The existence of exchange between MnO_2 and salt solutions requires that MnO_2 electrodes must first be equilibrated with the solution in which it is desired to use them before measurements of potential are made, and that this pre-equilibration must be repeated whenever the solution concentration is changed.

Alkali metal cation exchange studies on hydrous $MnO(OH)_2$ have shown[19] the existence of a well-marked affinity series

$$Cs^+ > NH_4^+ > K^+ > Na^+ > Li^+$$

similar to that found on other inorganic exchangers; saturation was reached at 10^{-2} mg Cs/mg $MnO(OH)_2$, corresponding to a capacity of 0.73 meq/g.

Mixed oxides can be prepared in which a second cation of higher charge than the parent cation is introduced into the structure, the resulting net positive charge being balanced by the presence of anions other than oxide and hydroxide; many of these are found to exchange the balancing anions reversibly[92]. Examples of such materials include $Zn(OH)_2$ in which Zn^{++} is partly replaced by Al^{+++}, and $Al(OH)_3$ containing Si^{++++}, Ti^{++++} or Zr^{++++}, the general formulae being $Zn_{1-n}Al_n(OH)_2X_n$ and $Al_{1-n}M_n^{IV}(OH)_3X_n$, where M^{IV} is a tetravalent cation and X^- a monovalent anion. For example, on addition of sodium hydroxide containing dissolved silica to a solution of aluminium chloride a product is obtained with the composition $Al_{0.86}Si_{0.14}(OH)_3Cl_{0.13}$. When heated to 150 °C water is lost (in the case of the chloride form HCl also) and the exchange capacity becomes negligible. The latter varies with the pH in unfired materials, and amphoteric behaviour has been observed for the alumina–silica exchanger; on absorbing long-chain organic anions such as stearate the materials are converted to hydrophobic solids. Apart from the fact that they are amorphous, they display striking formal similarities to the clays and zeolites.

QUADRIVALENT METAL OXIDES

Although the absorptive power of silica towards certain cations has been utilised for many years in removing impurities from solution, and although the absorption of dyes and of various cations by oxides such as thoria[91] have been explained on the basis of ion exchange involving surface hydroxyl groups, it is only within recent years that a systematic study has been made of the ion-exchange properties of quadrivalent metal oxides such as SiO_2, SnO_2, TiO_2, ThO_2 and ZrO_2. Strictly speaking, the materials employed do not possess the simple oxide formulae given above, since unless they are ignited at high temperatures they are found to contain varying amounts of water; the latter is not present as water of hydration, since on heating it is lost continuously over a range of temperatures instead of exhibiting dehydration isobars characteristic of hydrated compounds. Consequently these oxides are usually described as hydrous oxides; their structure is considered in more detail later (p. 97). In some cases, *e.g.* SiO_2 gel, the presence of hydroxyl groups in the structure has been shown by measurements of their infra-red spectra and by exchange of the hydrogen in these groups by deuterium when the solid is equilibrated with heavy water.

In principle the quadrivalent metal oxides may behave either as cation or anion exchangers, depending upon the basicity of the central metal atom and the strength of the metal–oxygen bond relative to that of the oxygen–hydrogen bond in the hydroxyl group. It is still not clear which of the following two mechanisms best represents the situation:

Acid solution   *Alkaline solution*

$$\geq\overset{+}{M} + OH^- \leftrightharpoons \geq M—OH \rightleftharpoons \geq M—\bar{O} + H^+$$

$$\geq M—\overset{+}{O}H_2 \overset{H^+}{\leftrightharpoons} \geq M—OH \overset{OH^-}{\rightleftharpoons} \geq M—\bar{O} + H_2O$$

Except for metals of low basicity (*e.g.* silicon) there is thus a transition from anion exchange in acid solution to cation exchange in alkaline solution, with the transition from one type of behaviour to another occurring over a range of pH depending upon the basicity of the metal ion. The absence of a sharp transition corresponding to this change (*cf.* the isoelectric point in amphoteric ions), and the existence in some cases of both cation and anion exchange at a given pH, suggest that the exchange sites may be heterogeneous.

Hydrous silica exhibits cation exchange properties only[20], the high electron affinity of the tetravalent silicon ion resulting in a very low basicity for the hydroxyl group; the hydrogen atoms of the latter are readily replaced by cations even in acid solution, particularly by ions which readily coordinate with oxygen. A well-marked affinity series exists, as shown by the curves in Fig. 24; from these it can be seen that separations are possible by suitably controlling the pH of the solution. The technique has been used[21] to separate uranium, plutonium and the trivalent fission products from solutions prepared by dissolving irradiated uranium in acid. Measurements of the distribution coefficient for uranyl ions as a function of acidity show that the exchange equilibrium obeys the law of mass action (p. 3), and the saturation capacity is found to be 1.2–1.4 meq/g. Studies of the rate of uptake show that cations may be grouped into two classes: those with charges up to $+3$ (Na^+, Ca^{++}, UO_2^{++}, Gd^{+++} etc.) are rapidly exchanged, while more highly-charged ions (Zr^{IV}, U^{IV}, Pu^{IV}) are absorbed slowly except from freshly-prepared solutions. The slow uptake of the latter ions from aged solutions is ascribed to their presence as hydrolysed and partly polymerized species, which must first be converted to simple species before they can undergo exchange.

Other quadrivalent oxides such as SnO_2, ThO_2, TiO_2 and ZrO_2

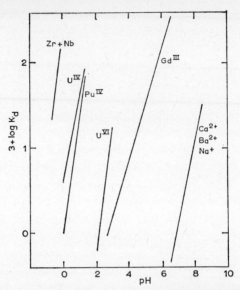

Fig. 24. Distribution coefficients for various ions on silica gel as a function of pH[20]. SiO_2:Kebo 50–100 mesh. Zr, Nb 1.1 mM; U^{IV} 2.0; Pu^{IV} 0.01; U^{VI} 1.0; Gd^{III} 0.092; Ca^{++} 25; Ba^{++} 25; Na^+ 30. [Reproduced, with permission, from *Acta Chem. Scand.*, 14 (1960) 1059.]

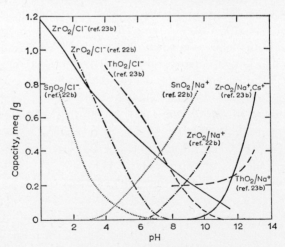

Fig. 25. Anion and cation exchange capacities of hydrous ZrO_2, ThO_2 and SnO_2 as a function of pH.

possess both cation and anion-exchange properties, depending upon the pH of the solution; owing to the lower basicity of tin the transition from anion- to cation-exchange behaviour occurs at a lower pH in SnO_2 than in ThO_2 or ZrO_2[22,23(b)], as shown in Fig. 25. Although under acid conditions ThO_2 and ZrO_2 behave as anion exchangers, they are also capable of absorbing cations which readily form bonds with oxygen, i.e. those which are prone to hydrolysis, such as UO_2^{++}, Fe^{+++}, Cr^{+++}, and to a lesser extent bivalent transition metal cations such as Ni^{++} and Cu^{++}. These may be absorbed from solution at pH values in the range 2–5[23(a),93].

Hydrous zirconium dioxide and similar oxides may be prepared by precipitation from acid solutions of the appropriate salts with alkali, when under suitable conditions flocculent or gelatinous precipitates are formed; on drying these yield granular products[23(b)] which are stable in aqueous suspensions except at acidities greater than 0.1 N. The capacity of ZrO_2 dried at temperatures below 100 °C is $\sim$ 1 meq/g, but this decreases markedly as the drying temperature is increased[24] (Table 22). Measurements of anion-exchange equilibria between Br^- and NO_3^- ions show that the law of mass action is followed[22(b)], while the rates of uptake of ions on ZrO_2 and ThO_2 are characteristic of processes controlled by diffusion within the solid (p. 128).

TABLE 22

CAPACITY OF HYDROUS ZrO_2 DRIED AT DIFFERENT TEMPERATURES[24]

Drying temperature	Uptake of CrO_4^{2-}(*) m moles/g	Uptake of Na^+(†) m moles/g
32 °C	1.31	0.80
105	1.25	0.72
202	0.91	0.63
320	0.45	0.50
500	0.15	0.18
800	0.05	0.05

* from 0.1 M K_2CrO_4 + 0.2 M HCl
† from 0.1 M NaOH

TABLE 23

CAPACITY OF BASIC LEAD SULPHATE AS A FUNCTION OF pH[25]

pH	Anion exchange capacity, meq/g	Cation exchange capacity, meq/g
1	8.5	—
1.7	5.8_5	—
5.6	2.0_4	—
6.1	1.8_5	—
6.3	1.0	0.1_1
6.7	0.8_2	—
7.2	—	0.1_9
9.0	—	2.4_5
10.0	—	5.4
11.0	—	7.2
12.5	—	7.5

A related material of high exchange capacity is basic lead sulphate[25], in which the exchange properties are undoubtedly due to the hydroxyl groups while the sulphate ion provides the necessary insolubility. Tribasic lead sulphate is an anion exchanger in acid solution and a cation exchanger in alkaline solution, with maximum capacities of 7–9 meq/g (Table 23). It may be used to remove trace radioactive elements from waste solutions, and appears to be very selective for rare earth elements; in the latter case, measurements of distribution coefficients suggest that it may be possible to use it for simple separations of rare earth mixtures.

INSOLUBLE SALTS OF POLYBASIC METALS: ZIRCONIUM PHOSPHATE

Zirconium phosphate may be prepared either by precipitation with phosphoric acid, or solutions of soluble phosphates, from acid solutions of suitable zirconium salts (*e.g.* zirconyl chloride or nitrate), or by treatment of zirconium oxide with phosphoric acid. In the latter case, the uptake of phosphate is irreversible and is considerably in excess of the anion exchange capacity of the oxide[22,26,27]. The former method of preparation is the one usually employed. It was first demonstrated by Boyd et al.[1] that columns containing finely-divided zirconium phosphate supported on silica wool could be used to separate uranium and plutonium from fission products by an ion-exchange process, and the study of the cation-exchange properties of this and similar insoluble salts has since developed considerably. Many such salts are now known; among the metals studied have been zirconium, thorium, titanium, cerium, aluminium, tin (IV), bismuth, chromium and tantalum, and the anions employed include phosphate, arsenate, antimonate, vanadate, molybdate, tungstate, chromate, silicate, sulphide, oxalate and carbonate. Most of the work to date has however been concerned with zirconium phosphate, which has been more thoroughly studied than any of the other materials.

Preparation of Zirconium Phosphate

The physical form of zirconium phosphate prepared by precipitation varies according to the method employed, but two principal types may be distinguished. A finely-divided, microcrystalline form in which the ratio of phosphate to zirconium is approximately 2:1 (corresponding to zirconyl dihydrogen phosphate, $ZrO(H_2PO_4)_2$) is produced by slowly adding the reactants (e.g. zirconyl nitrate solution and phosphoric acid) to a well-stirred, heated dilute sulphuric acid solution[28]. The slow precipitation under conditions where neither reagent is greatly in excess of the other, and where the solubility of the product is high relative to room temperature conditions, leads to the growth of fine crystals which are too small themselves to be used in ion-exchange columns, but which may be pelleted under pressure without a binder and then granulated[29]. If, however, the reagents are mixed rapidly at room temperature, rapid precipitation ensues, and a gelatinous precipitate is formed which settles extremely slowly until it has been thoroughly washed by decantation to remove the stabilising counter-ions which prevent coagulation of the precipitate[26,30]. After washing, the product may be filtered to give a gelatinous cake, which shrinks on drying and cracks to give a granular product resembling silica gel; the final product may be either opaque and white, or glassy and transparent. On immersion in water the granules break down along strain lines with the release of air bubbles which have been entrapped in the gel, to give a granular material which is completely stable physically in water, and which may be obtained in a range of mesh sizes from several millimetres downwards. The precise conditions which govern the physical nature of the product are not well understood, although extensive work has been carried out on the effects of varying the method of preparation[31]. It is known that hard, glassy products tend to be formed from dilute zirconium solutions, and that concentrated solutions produce a softer, chalk-like material. Similarly, although nitrate solutions in general favour the formation of opaque granular materials, sulphate solutions give glassy products in which the rate of uptake of cations, particularly polyvalent ones, is much lower. In general the granular products formed by rapid precipitation have a phosphate : zirconium ratio less than $2 : 1$[26,27,31] and are of rather indefinite composition. The ratio in the solid increases towards a limiting figure of ~ 1.7 as the corresponding ratio in the reacting solutions is increased, and at low values of the latter (0.5–1.0) it is possible to precipitate solids which still contain in addition to phosphate the anion originally present in the zirconium solution[26]. The original anion may be reversibly displaced by other anions, the product thus exhibiting both cation and anion-exchange properties.

Veselý and Pekárek have shown[32] that even under conditions where phosphate is considerably in excess the composition of the product may depend upon the conditions of preparation. With Na_3PO_4 as precipitant the ratio of $PO_4 : Zr$ in the product prepared from $ZrOCl_2$ in 0.1 N HCl was only 0.69 compared with 1.29 for precipitation with H_3PO_4 in 0.1 N HCl, both solutions having a $PO_4 : Zr$ ratio of 1.5. Similarly, precipitation with phosphoric acid from a 6 N HCl solution of $ZrOCl_2$ gave a product in which $PO_4 : Zr$ did not exceed 1.66, whereas in the absence of hydrochloric acid the ratio was 1.86 and could be increased to ~ 2.0 by digestion at 60 °C with 20% H_3PO_4, followed by washing with water until the washings gave a negative reaction for phosphate. These results suggest an explanation for the variation in the composition of the products reported by Baetslé and Pelsemaekers[27], who used 6 N HCl, and those of Nancollas and Paterson[29] and of Larsen and Vissars[33], both of whom used less acid solutions and reported higher ratios of PO_4:Zr in their materials than did the first two authors. Samples prepared by Veselý and Pekárek by precipitation from 6 N HCl solutions were found to contain up to 2.9% of chloride, which could be removed by repeated washing with water, presumably by replacement with hydroxyl groups; conversely, samples of high phosphate content (PO_4:Zr = 1.8–2.0) prepared in the absence of HCl were found after digestion with 4 N HCl to have a lower phsophate content and to contain appreciable quantities of chloride. The findings of Veselý and Pekárek do not, however, completely explain the differences in composition observed by various authors, since in many cases ratios of $\sim$ 1.7–1.8 are obtained for products in which no anion other than phosphate can be detected.

Zirconium phosphate may also be prepared in the form of spherical beads by adopting the techniques used to produce various spherical cracking catalysts such as thorium phosphate[34] and sodium aluminosilicate[35]. Two basic methods have been employed. In the first[36] zirconyl nitrate solution and phosphoric acid are mixed rapidly and sprayed into a column of mineral oil; precipitation takes place within the spherical droplets as they fall through the oil phase, and by careful choice of conditions precipitation is complete and the droplet gelled by the time it passes to an aqueous layer at the foot of the column. After washing and drying in air at 300 °C beads of 2 mm diameter were obtained by this method. In the second method[37] the onset and rate of precipitation were controlled by complexing zirconium with citrate ion before mixing with phosphoric acid and spraying into an oil column; by selecting suitable proportions of citrate and zirconium the onset of precipitation may be delayed for any chosen period. Similar methods may be used to prepare spherical beads of ZrO_2 using NH_4OH instead of phosphoric acid, and in principle the technique could be applied to any exchanger of this class.

Physical and Chemical Properties of Zirconium Phosphate

Granular zirconium phosphate shows striking physical stability in water even at elevated temperatures; although some breakdown occurs it is slow and not catastrophic, and particle size distribution measurements after prolonged exposure to water at 300 °C show that the material could be used for extended periods at this temperature[23(a),36]. After prolonged washing with water, products with $PO_4 : Zr < 2 : 1$ still give an acid reaction due to hydrolysis of phosphate, and in alkaline solutions the replacement of phosphate by hydroxyl ion is appreciable, particularly at high temperatures. The stability of zirconium phosphate towards hydrolysis at $pH > 7$ appears to vary according to the method of preparation,

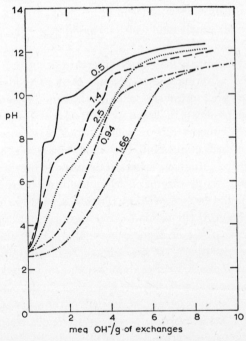

Fig. 26. pH titration curves for different preparations of zirconium phosphate. $PO_4 : Zr$ in reagents $= 0.5$, 1.4 and 2.5 [Amphlett, McDonald and Redman[26]]. $PO_4 : Zr$ in product $= 0.94$ and 1.66 [Baetslé and Pelsmaekers[27]].

but is invariably greater than that of zirconium tungstate or molybdate, which are hydrolysed extensively at pH 7–8. The solubility of zirconium phosphate in 10 M HCl is given[38] as $\sim 2 \cdot 10^{-5}$ M, which, although low, is much higher than that of ZrO_2 in water ($< 10^{-6}$ M). Zirconium phosphate is extremely resistant to acids other than HF, H_2SO_4 and oxalic acid, all of which complex zirconium very effectively; on the other hand, zirconium oxide dissolves in acids but is stable in alkaline solutions.

pH-titrations of zirconium phosphate having the ideal formula with a phosphate:zirconium ratio of 2:1 show only monofunctional acid behaviour in the acid phosphate groups (Fig. 26), but with the phosphate-deficient materials more complex titration curves are frequently obtained which suggest that in this case the material may be polyfunctional. Zirconium oxide behaves as a monofunctional base on titration with acid solutions.

The Structures of Zirconium oxide and Phosphate

Because of the poor degree of crystallinity exhibited even by microcrystalline zirconium phosphate, and of the completely amorphous nature of granular zirconium oxide and phosphate prepared by rapid precipitation, opinion on the structures of these materials is based largely on analogy with data on the structures of complex zirconium ions present in aqueous solution. X-ray studies on granular hydrous zirconia[36] show that as the drying temperature is increased the structure begins to show signs of crystallinity at $\sim$ 300 °C, and at 1000 °C the pattern is identical with that reported for monoclinic ZrO_2. Similar studies on granular zirconium phosphate show that the amorphous structure persists until at least 500 °C, but that at 1000 °C the pattern is characteristic of zirconium pyrophosphate, ZrP_2O_7; this is, however, known to be not chemically identical with the original material. These changes are accompanied by an irreversible loss of water from the material. Although the details relating to loss of water on heating vary for different samples from one author to another[27,29,36] the salient features are that neither oxide nor phosphate gives evidence of the existence of discrete hydrates. In the phosphate the total water loss on heating to 1000 °C is $\sim$ 20%, and constitutional water is lost at temperatures in excess of 300 °C, presumably due to the condensation of acid phosphate groups to pyrophosphate. The loss of capacity of zirconium dioxide on firing to $>$ 300° coincides with the transition temperature from the tetragonal to the mono-clinic structure (290 °C) and may be due to recrystallization of the material in a more compact form.

Evidence in favour of the condensation of acid phosphate groups to pyrophosphate on heating is furnished by the infra-red spectra of different samples of zirconium phosphate[32]. Spectra of materials with ratios of PO_4:Zr equal to 1.7 and 1.95 after heating to 1000 °C for 24 h are similar to that of cubic zirconium pyrophosphate ZrP_2O_7[39,40] while material with PO_4:Zr $=$ 1.0 gives a pattern resembling that from a product formed on heating ZrO_2 and ZrP_2O_7 to 1200 °C, which may be ascribable to zirconyl pyrophosphate, $(ZrO)_2P_2O_7$. Condensation of the acid phosphate groups was fol-lowed at different temperatures for zirconium phosphate with PO_4:Zr $=$ 1.95 by examining the characteristic P–O–P frequency range of 958–983 cm^{-1}; the spectra showed not only that condensa-tion is complete at 850 °C, but that it commences at a temperature which is at least as low as 260 °C. Comparison of the spectra with those of mixtures of zirconium phosphate and pyrophosphate sug-gests that $\sim$ 20% of the phosphate groups are condensed at 260° and $\sim$ 60% at 450 °C. It is possible therefore that at least part of the weight loss at relatively low temperatures is due to constitu-tional water formed on condensation of acid phosphate groups. When zirconium phosphate is converted to the sodium or potassium form and heated to 1000 °C the characteristic P–O–P frequency is strongly suppressed, indicating that the substitution of Na$^+$ or K$^+$ for H$^+$ on the acid phosphate groups hinders condensation of the latter.

Zirconium is rarely found even in dilute aqueous solutions as the simple ion Zr^{4+} or as the zirconyl ion ZrO^{2+}, but is generally present in either complexed or hydrolysed forms in which polymeric species may predominate; this generalization is particularly valid in the relatively concentrated solutions which are used in the preparation of zirconium oxide and phosphate. It is natural, therefore, to attempt to explain the structures of the latter products on the basis of the ions from which they are formed. Even in fairly dilute solutions pH-titration and ultracentrifuge studies have shown[41] that zirconium exists as hydrolysed species such as $ZrOOH^+$, while in more concentrated solutions in HCl trimeric and tetrameric ions such as $[(ZrO)_3(OH)_3]^{3+}$ and $[(ZrO)_4(OH)_4]^{4+}$ have been observed. Other evidence based on the coagulation of negative AgBr and AgI sols also supports the existence of highly-charged, hydrolysed polymers containing up to three zirconium atoms in each ion[42]. Direct evidence is provided by X-ray scattering studies on aqueous solutions of zirconium and hafnium oxyhalides[43] which indicate the presence of structures such as $[M_4(OH)_8(H_2O)_{16}]X_8$, where M is zirconium or hafnium and X is the halide ion; the structures postulated are similar to those found in the crystalline oxyhalides[44], and the results suggest that even higher polymers than the tetramer may be present. The existence of tetrameric species in solution is also in accord with X-ray studies on basic salts of tetravalent metals such as Ti, Zr and Th[45] prepared by hydrothermal synthesis at 50–250 °C. These indicate the presence of chains of polymers such as $[Zr_4(OH)_6CrO_4]_n^{8+}$; while data on the titanium derivatives suggest that in titanium solutions there are chains such as $(-TiO-)_n^{2n+}$, in the case of zirconium hydrolysis and polymerization appear to produce networks with –O–Zr–O– bridges which are cross-linked on each alternate zirconium atom.

Turning now to the chemical evidence from which deductions may be drawn regarding structure and composition, the dehydration isobars and thermogravimetric experiments reveal the absence of definite hydrates in the hydrous oxides, and we may assume[46] that when the oxides are precipitated the ion $ZrOOH^+$ is incorporated as a repeating unit in the structure:

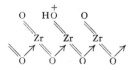

Exchangeable counter-ions would be incorporated to maintain charge neutrality when the above positively-charged polyelectrolyte cation is precipitated. Similar considerations apply to hydrous thoria, since hydrolysis studies in solution show the formation of polymeric ions of the formula $Th[(OH)_3Th]_n^{(n+4)+}$. In alkaline solutions where the oxides behave as cation exchangers, neutralisation of the oxonium ion grouping and coordination of OH^- ions may occur.

Chemical evidence in the case of zirconium phosphate is conflicting at present, and the structure and composition probably vary according to the mode of preparation. Paterson[46] has described a material in which the ratio of phosphate to zirconium is $2:1$, corresponding to diphosphatozirconic acid[47]:

This gives a smooth monofunctional titration curve, unlike the granular gels, and on continued washing only phosphate ion is found in solution, indicating a slow hydrolysis of the material. Conversion of the hydrogen form to the caesium form results in the loss of 2.5 m moles of water per meq of exchange capacity; in support of this observation the loss of water per milliequivalent on heating to 250 °C is 11 m moles for the hydrogen form and 8 for the caesium form. In contrast to this behaviour, the same water content was observed for several different anionic forms of hydrous ZrO_2. Comparison of the observed capacity of ~ 0.6 meq/g for the above sample of zirconium phosphate in acid solution with that calculated for complete utilization of the hydrogen atoms suggests that only one hydrogen atom in ten is available for exchange under these conditions, although in alkaline solution, where the capacity is much higher, approximately half of the hydrogen atoms appear to be utilised.

The materials prepared by Baetslé and Pelsemaekers[27], although originally tending to a limiting ratio of phosphate to zirconium of $2:1$ in the freshly-prepared precipitates when phosphate was in appreciable excess, tended on continuous washing to approach a limiting composition in which $PO_4 : Zr = 1.67$, suggesting that the latter material may contain a trimeric unit based upon the structure $[(ZrO)_3(OH)_3]^{3+}$ in which phosphate groups have replaced hydroxyl groups. Thermogravimetric data, which differ somewhat from those of Nancollas and Paterson, suggest that three water molecules are associated with each trimer, while in agreement with other workers[26] pH titrations reveal a weakly acid grouping with $pK_a \simeq 3$, suggesting that in acid solution only the first ionization of the $-H_2PO_4$ group is observed. In conjunction with the observed maximum capacity of 4.3 ± 0.1 meq/g in alkaline solution, these facts lead Baetslé to suggest the following structure:

$$\left[\begin{array}{ccccccc} H_2PO_3 \cdot O & & H_2PO_3 \cdot O & & OH & & O \\ | & H_2O & | & H_2O & | & H_2O & \| \\ | \swarrow & & | \swarrow & & | \swarrow & & \\ \text{---}Zr\text{---}O\text{---} & & Zr\text{---}O\text{---} & & Zr\text{---}O\text{---}P\text{---}O\text{---} \\ | & & | & & | & & | \\ OH & & H_2PO_3 \cdot O & & H_2PO_3 \cdot O & & OH \end{array}\right]_n$$

This would exhibit a maximum capacity of 4.56 meq/g if only the phosphate groups are involved, or 6.84 if in addition exchange can take place at the hydroxyl groups, which is much less likely.

Similar considerations have been advanced by Michael[36], in which phosphate groups are assumed to replace coordinatively-bonded water molecules (but not hydroxyl groups or oxygen atoms) in trimeric units to give a ratio of $PO_4 : Zr = 1.67$ (experimental value after prolonged washing $= 1.63$) and a capacity of 0.67 moles of Cs^+ ion per mole of zirconium. On heating, the material prepared in acid solution produced zirconium pyrophosphate, ZrP_2O_7, while that from alkaline solution appeared to give the orthophosphate $Zr_3(PO_4)_4$. Although in both instances the results appear to be well substantiated, the recent work of Veselý and Pekárek[32] indicates that the range of composition and structures may be quite wide, and that they may be very sensitive to the method of preparation.

Recent studies indicate[97] how widely the properties may change when the conditions of preparation are varied, and they also give some

indication of a possible structure for one form of crystalline zirconium phosphate. In this work, zirconium phosphate gel was first
prepared by adding an acid solution of zirconyl chloride to excess
phosphoric acid. The gelatinous precipitate was allowed to stand
overnight in contact with the solution before it was filtered, washed
and dried. Thermogravimetric analyses showed that the solid, which
possessed the composition $ZrO_2 \cdot P_2O_5 \cdot 2H_2O$, lost one molecule of
water at 100–135 °C and a second at 240–350 °C. The original product
was either amorphous or poorly crystalline, and on heating to 700 °C
a poorly crystalline zirconium pyrosphosphate phase was identified
by X-ray crystallography; on annealing at 900 °C the crystallinity
of this phase was greatly improved. Conversion to pyrophosphate
occurred at much lower temperatures in the presence of excess phosphate. On refluxing the gel with phosphoric acid, a well-crystallized
zirconium phosphate was obtained, its composition also being $ZrO_2 \cdot$
$P_2O_5 \cdot 2H_2O$. This material lost one molecule of water reversibly
on heating to 80–120 °C with little change in the X-ray pattern. At
300–650 °C a second molecule was lost; at 450 °C a disordered zirconium phosphate phase was identified, which was converted to pyrophosphate on further heating to 700–750 °C. The crystalline zirconium
phosphate lost negligible amounts of phosphate on being washed
with water.

The ion-exchange behaviour of these products differs from that
of samples prepared by other workers, in that the crystalline material gave two sharp endpoints on pH-titration with NaCl/NaOH
solutions, corresponding to ratio of Na : Zr of 1 : 1 and 2 : 1; the
maximum capacity was $\sim$ 5.1 meq/g. The gel gave a less well defined
titration curve with several inflexions, and moreover was hydrolysed
extensively at pH > 7.5. Lithium, sodium and potassium were all
readily exchanged, but no uptake of caesium was observed. X-ray data
showed that the structure remained unchanged until the ratio Na : Zr
equalled 1 : 1; beyond this value there was evidence of lattice expansion.

In interpreting these results the authors suggest the formula
$Zr(HPO_4)_2 \cdot H_2O$, rather than $ZrO(H_2PO_4)_2$ (cf. p. 100); the former
possesses two replaceable hydrogen atoms per molecule, and would be

more likely to lose water reversibly at low temperatures without a drastic change in the X-ray pattern. Preliminary examination of the X-ray data suggests that the crystalline material is composed of sheets of phosphate units in which some of the oxygen atoms are bound to zirconium atoms while others carry hydrogen atoms. Half of the P–OH groups form hydrogen bonds with phosphate groups in adjacent layers, while the others are hydrogen-bonded to water molecules. The combined X-ray and titration data suggest that ion exchange occurs in two stages. In the first, hydrogen ions are displaced from the P–OH groups which are bonded to water molecules, *viz.*

$$P\text{–OH}\ldots.OH_2 + M^+ \rightleftharpoons P\text{–}\overset{-}{O}\text{–}\overset{+}{M} + H_3O^+$$

The interlayer spacing remains unchanged until the ratio M:Zr equals 1 : 1, after which hydrogen ions are replaced in P–OH groups which are bonded to adjacent layers, leading to an increase in spacing. Failure to observe exchange with caesium is attributed to the fact that the first stage of exchange cannot occur with such a large cation, since the lattice cannot expand to accommodate it. The difference between the behaviour of the gel and that of the crystalline product is considered to be due to the former possessing a more disordered structure. The larger interplanar spacings and weaker interlayer hydrogen bonds in the gel will permit exchange of caesium ions, and will also favour hydrolysis of the phosphate groups; moreover, the hydrogen bonds would be expected to possess a range of bond energies, leading to a poorly-defined titration curve.

Although there are points of detail in which this work differs from that of other authors, notably with regard to caesium-exchange and to stability towards hydrolysis, it indicates the need for a combined attack on the problem using several techniques; it also suggests that one of the conditions of preparation which merits careful examination is the effect of ageing the precipitate, either by standing in contact with the supernatant solution or by boiling with phosphoric acid. Other evidence which suggests that phase changes may occur on prolonged contact with solutions at high temperatures, leading apparently to loss of ion-exchange properties, is described elsewhere (p. 107).

It is clear that the structure, and even the composition, of this class of exchangers is subject to considerable doubt; data on materials other than zirconium phosphate are inadequate to enable us to do more than conjecture that their structures are probably analogous to that of the latter. The structures which have been tentatively proposed for the phosphate contain linear polymeric chains, whereas the physical stability, resistance to swelling, and ionic sieve effects[48] which are observed suggest that the structure is a robust three-dimensional network similar to that of the cage-like zeolites (p. 43) rather than a fibrous or lamellar one. It may be that the unit is best represented by a cyclic polymer such as that of Clearfield and Vaughan[44], rather than a linear one of the Kraus–Johnson type, with oxygen or hydroxyl bridges between pairs of zirconium atoms.

Ion Exchange in Zirconium Phosphate

Chemical and infra-red spectral evidence suggests that ion exchange in zirconium phosphate involves replaceable hydrogen atoms in acid phosphate groupings which play a role analogous to that of the sulphonic acid groups of strongly-acid cation-exchange resins. The acidity of the phosphoric acid groups is intermediate between those of the fully-ionised sulphonic groups of strong acid resins and of the very weakly acid carboxylic groups in weak acid resins; thus zirconium phosphate behaves as an efficient cation exchanger in acid solutions, whereas weak acid resins such as Amberlite IRC–50 function only at pH > 7. In acid solutions the release of hydrogen ions on treating zirconium phosphate with a salt solution is equal to the amount of cations absorbed, but in alkaline solution the hydrolytic reaction prevents a balance from being obtained. The capacity is independent of particle size and depends only on the mass of material, and a study of the uptake as a function of concentration for pairs of cations (Fig. 27) shows that the law of mass action is obeyed[49]. If we consider two ions, M^{n+} and H^+, competing for the exchanger, then in sufficiently dilute solutions, where activity coefficients may be neglected, we may write for the equilibrium

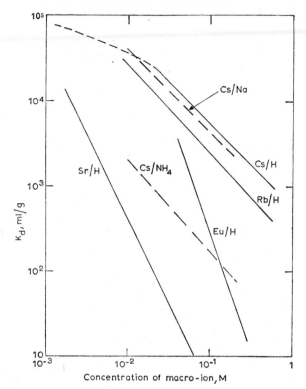

Fig. 27. Distribution coefficients for tracer ions on zirconium phosphate in the presence of different macro-ions[49].

$$M^{n+} + n\,HX \rightleftharpoons n\,H^+ + M^{n+}(X^-)_n$$

the expression

$$K_H{}^M = \frac{[\overline{M}^{n+}]\,[H^+]^n}{[M^{n+}]\,[\overline{H}^+]^n}$$

using the terminology described earlier (p. 24). If $[M^{n+}] \ll [H^+]$, as in tracer solutions of the ion M^{n+}, the variation in $[\overline{H}^+]$ may be neglected and we may write for the distribution coefficient of M^{n+} at equilibrium

$$K_d{}^M = \frac{[\overline{M^{n+}}]}{[M^{n+}]} = K_H{}^M \frac{[\overline{H^+}]^n}{[H^+]^n} \simeq \frac{K_1}{[H^+]^n}$$

If the law of mass action is obeyed, a plot of log $K_d{}^M$ *versus* log [H$^+$] will be a straight line of slope $-n$; in the cases given in Fig. 27 the slopes are -1, -1, -2 and -3 for the ion pairs Cs$^+$/H$^+$, Rb$^+$/H$^+$, Sr^{2+}/H$^+$ and Eu^{3+}/H$^+$.

The saturation capacity of zirconium phosphate increases from ~ 0.5 meq/g in acid solution to values as high as 5–6 in alkaline solution; other exchangers of this class behave similarly, although capacities may vary from one to another and even between different preparations of the same exchanger (Fig. 28). On drying at elevated temperatures there is usually some loss of capacity in acid solution when water is lost irreversibly in the conversion of acid phosphate groups to pyrophosphate at temperatures in excess of 350 °C, although the capacity in alkaline solution may be partly

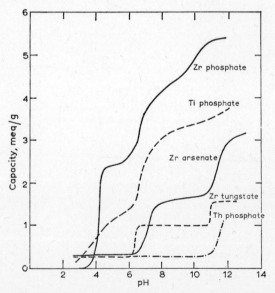

Fig. 28. Cation exchange capacity of some synthetic inorganic exchangers as a function of pH[23a]. [Reproduced by permission of the United Nations Organisation.]

regained[26]. There is evidence[36] that this water may be regained, together with complete recovery of the capacity, if the material is immersed in solutions at 300 °C, even after drying at 1000 °C. Zirconium molybdate and tungstate are much more sensitive to drying at elevated temperatures than is the phosphate, and the tungstate loses its capacity completely on drying at 100 °C. Zirconium phosphate retains its ion-exchange properties in solutions at 300 °C, the exchange being reversible provided that the temperature is not lowered[50]; it appears however[51] that even simple cations such as K^+ which have been exchanged at 300 °C may become fixed in the lattice if the system is allowed to cool to room temperature. This behaviour may be associated with structural changes, since the water content of the dried material is reduced by this treatment.

Selectivity in Zirconium Phosphate

In zirconium phosphate the selectivity for univalent cations follows a pattern similar to that in the sulphonic acid resins, *viz.*

$$Li^+ < Na^+ < K^+, NH_4^+ < Rb^+ < Cs^+$$

Although the values of distribution coefficients reported by different workers differ in detail[22,26,49] this sequence is preserved

TABLE 24

DISTRIBUTION COEFFICIENTS ON ZIRCONIUM PHOSPHATE
(ACID FORM)[26]

Cation	Solution concentration	K_d ml/g
Li^+	0.014 N	17
Na^+	0.014 N	36
K^+	0.014 N	84
Rb^+	0.013 N	182
Cs^+	0.013 N	200
Mg^{2+}	0.014 N	20
Ca^{2+}	0.014 N	56
Sr^{2+}	0.012 N	63
Ba^{2+}	0.014 N	91

(Table 24). Caesium and rubidium are very strongly absorbed relative to the other alkali metals, as also is thallous ion, but not silver; data have also been given[52] for the absorption of caesium and francium ions on zirconium phosphate, molybdate and tungstate. The alkaline earth cations are generally less strongly absorbed from acid solution, and the rare earths less strongly still, and good separations are possible among the various classes (see below). Caesium is very strongly absorbed even in strongly acid solutions and in the presence of a considerable excess of polyvalent cations, as shown by the data in Fig. 29, which refer to a sample having $PO_4:Zr = 1.74$ and a capacity of 2.2 ± 0.1 meq/g at pH 5, prepared[53] by adding excess phosphoric acid to a solution of $ZrOCl_2$ in $1\ M$ HCl. Uranyl ions are more strongly absorbed than the other bivalent cations (cf. SiO_2, p. 90).

Distribution coefficients have been reported[32] for a number of

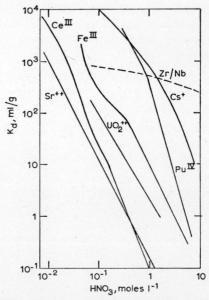

Fig. 29. Distribution coefficients of several cations in nitric acid solution on zirconium phosphate[53]. [Reproduced, with permission, from *Bull. Boris Kidrich Inst.*, 13 (1962) 1.]

TABLE 25

DISTRIBUTION COEFFICIENTS ON ZIRCONIUM PHOSPHATE AS A
FUNCTION OF DRYING TEMPERATURE AND OF PO_4:Zr RATIO[32]

| Cation | K_d, ml/g | | | | | |
| | PO_4:Zr = 1.0 | | | PO_4:Zr = 1.87 | | |
	40°	260°	1000° C	40°	260°	1000° C
Na^+	—	—	—	10.0	8.8	—
K^+	9.5	8.0	9.6	19.5	21.0	3.7
Cs^+	26.3	14.8	10.0	349	126	4.3
Sr^{2+}	—	—	—	1.0	<1	—
ZrO^{2+}	361	252	2.5	1400	450	24.0
UO_2^{2+}	<1	—	—	897	176	—
Ce^{3+}	5.1	2.6	1.6	43.5	3.9	2.7
Fe^{3+}	37.9	34.2	<1	6570	315	3.7
Bi^{3+}	700	219	<1	>8000	1000	8.7
$RuNO^{3+}$	5.3	—	—	5.8	—	—
Th^{4+}	130	75	<1	2760	504	5.5
Pu^{4+}	1290	359	16.0	5580	684	32.4

cations of different valencies on zirconium phosphate samples
having PO_4:Zr ratios of 1.0 and 1.87 at drying temperatures of
40°, 260° and 1000 °C. K_d is higher for the material of higher
phosphate content and generally decreases with increasing drying
temperature, although for some cations the uptake is still appreciable after drying at 1000 °C (Table 25). That this is not due to
re-formation of acid phosphate groups on immersion in water is
shown by the fact that the infra-red spectrum of material dried at
1000 °C does not change under these conditions. Although it is
conceivable that polyvalent cations such as Zr^{IV} and Pu^{IV}, which
form insoluble phosphates, can be absorbed by a mechanism other
than ion exchange on material which has been dried at 1000 °, it
is not readily apparent why the heavier alkali metal ions should
also be absorbed.

Ion-sieve Properties of Zirconium Phosphate[48]

The compact structure of zirconium phosphate, and the relatively small degree of swelling on conversion from the hydrogen form
to other cationic forms, suggest that it may exhibit ion-sieve prop-

TABLE 26

UPTAKE OF SUBSTITUTED AMMONIUM IONS ON ZIRCONIUM
PHOSPHATE[48]
(All values are relative to those for NH_4^+)

Cation	Equilibrium uptake	Saturation capacity	Equilibrium uptake corrected for reduction in capacity
$MeNH_3^+$	0.82	0.80	1.02
$EtNH_3^+$	0.78	0.74	1.05
$Pr^nNH_3^+$	0.68	0.72	0.94
$Pr^iNH_3^+$	0.68	0.63	1.09
$Bu^nNH_3^+$	0.62	0.57	1.09
$Pe^nNH_3^+$	0.56	0.56	1.00
$Pr^n_2NH_2^+$	0.50	0.50	1.00
$Bu^n_2NH_2^+$	0.39	—	—
NMe_4^+	0.72	0.56	1.27
NEt_4^+	0.53	0.43	1.23
NBu_4^+	0.30	—	—

erties similar to those of the zeolites (p. 49), and this has been confirmed by a study of the uptake of substituted ammonium ions on the material (Table 26). Both equilibrium uptake and saturation capacity were measured, in order to correct the former for any variations in the latter. When this is done, two types of steric hindrance are observed:

(i) for the ions NR_4^+, where R is an alkyl group, the uptake and capacity decrease as the substituent R increases in size, suggesting that the material possesses a heterogeneous structure in which some pores or channels are accessible only to smaller cations;

(ii) for n-alkylammonium or di-n-alkylammonium ions RNH_3^+ and $R\overset{+}{N}H_2R$, where the cation can assume an approximately linear configuration having a cross-sectional area similar to that of the NH_4^+ ion, the uptake decreases as the chain length of R is increased, but when normalised to take account of the decrease in capacity there is very little change. This suggests that longer chains, which when fully extended can enter pores or channels which are accessible to NH_4^+ ions, may block sites within the pores and so prevent full utilization of the available capacity.

OTHER EXCHANGERS OF THE ZIRCONIUM PHOSPHATE TYPE

A number of other cation exchangers may be prepared by precipitation methods similar to that employed for zirconium phosphate; these include thorium and titanium phosphates, zirconium arsenate, tungstate and molybdate. Thorium phosphate has also been prepared[54] by heating a solution of the nitrate with silica gel and absorbing phosphate on the thorium silicate so formed. These materials are generally inferior to zirconium phosphate in stability, *e.g.* titanium phosphate is readily hydrolysed at 200 ° in 1 *M* NH_4NO_3 solution[55], while zirconium molybdate and tungstate are appreciably hydrolysed at room temperature above neutral pH. Tantalum phosphate has been shown[55] to be severely hydrolysed in alkaline solution, while its capacity (0.6 meq/g in acid solution) is lost on drying at 200 °C. In general the capacity of zirconium phosphate is somewhat higher than that of the other members, and is much less affected on drying the material at temperatures up to 300 °C. Zirconium silicate has been prepared[56] by adding NH_4OH to a solution containing zirconyl chloride and sodium silicate; the gel may be washed and dried at 70–80 °C. Sharp breakthrough curves are obtained for caesium on this material, the maximum capacity of $\sim$ 1 meq/g corresponding to a mole ratio of $SiO_2:ZrO_2$ between 3 and 6. The silicate breaks down in dilute HCl, even after drying at 250 °C, with loss of $\sim$ 70% of its capacity. The capacity is also reduced, and zirconium released to solution, on autoclaving in water at 200 °C, but subsequent treatment with acid then has little effect. The capacity is increased by $\sim$ 30% on treatment with $(NH_4)_2HPO_4$, but the product is very unstable towards acid.

Several vanadates have been shown by Phillips and Kraus[57] to possess capacities between 0.5 and 2 meq/g in acid solution and show a moderate selectivity towards caesium and rubidium, the separation factor α_{Rb}^{Cs} being between 3 and 5. The rare earths were absorbed to varying extents, the distribution coefficients for cerium and europium in 0.1 M HNO$_3$ being < 1 for niobium vanadate and > 1000 for zirconium vanadate. Zirconium antimonate[58], prepared by adding ammonia to solutions of zirconyl chloride containing excess antimony pentachloride in hydrochloric acid, shows an interesting and unexplained reversal of selectivity, the order of elution of the alkali metals being Li$^+$, K$^+$, Rb$^+$, Cs$^+$, Na$^+$. Unlike zirconium phosphate, where sodium is removed even by washing with water, the antimonate absorbs sodium from acid solutions, and the latter cannot be eluted even with concentrated HNO$_3$, although it may be removed with 2 M NH$_4$NO$_3$. The product has a mole ratio Sb^V:Zr^{IV} of approximately 2:1 and is reasonably stable in dilute alkalies and acids; its capacity varies from ~ 0.5 meq/g in acid solution to ~ 5 meq/g in 0.9 N NaOH, while distribution coefficients from tracer solutions are greater than 10^4 and 10^3 for Sr^{2+} and Cs$^+$ ions respectively. Reference has also been made[59] to a number of mixed oxides of bismuth and other metals (Zr, Th, Sn^{IV}) which show high selectivities towards chloride ions in neutral solutions. A product stated to be phosphoantimonic acid[95], prepared by adding antimony pentachloride to phosphoric acid and drying at 80 °C, was found to exchange several monovalent and bivalent cations reversibly. Potassium was strongly absorbed, and was best eluted with 1 M ammonium salt solutions. pH-titrations showed the product to be a relatively strong monobasic acid comparable to HSb(OH)$_6$.

Several interesting zirconium-based exchangers have been reported by Russian workers[60] but in general their stability is rather limited. The chromate exhibited a capacity of 0.6 meq/g, independent of pH between 2 and 10; strontium and calcium were separated very efficiently, the enrichment factor for the former being $1.2 \cdot 10^5$. The oxalate and carbonate showed weakly acid properties similar to those of carboxylic resins; the former separated lanthanum and calcium efficiently and the latter calcium and magnesium. The sulphide, prepared by precipitation with excess sodium sulphide, was very selective for ions forming insoluble sulphides; it is a weak acid exchanger, the hydrogen form having a very low

capacity compared with other cationic forms. High enrichments
were obtained for copper relative to calcium and iron.

SOME CHEMICAL SEPARATIONS

Several interesting and highly efficient separations have been described using oxide and insoluble acid salt exchangers, although
clearly their full potential has still to be realised. Kraus has summarized a number of their properties with regard to separation as
follows[22(b)]:

(*i*) Most hydrous oxides greatly prefer polyvalent anions such
as chromate, borate, sulphate and phosphate to monovalent ones,
and subsequent removal of the former may require quite drastic
treatment, *e.g.* with NaOH solutions.

(*ii*) Alkali metals are held more strongly than the alkaline earths
on the hydrogen form of zirconium phosphate, but the order is

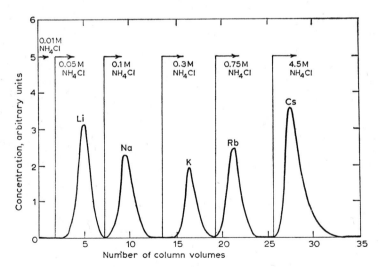

Fig. 30. Separation of the alkali metals at tracer concentration on zirconium
tungstate[61]. Column 0.13 cm² × 12.3 cm. Flow-rate ∼ 0.75 cm/min. [Reprod-
uced, with permission, from *Nature*, 177 (1956) 1128.]

reversed on the ammonium form. In neutral or weakly acid solutions the oxides absorb the rare earths, alkaline earths and alkali metals in that order of decreasing affinity.

(*iii*) Good separations may be achieved between individual alkali metals or alkaline earths on the hydrogen form of zirconium phosphate and similar exchangers. Here the heavier cations are more strongly held, and caesium may even be recovered from concentrated salt solutions such as 13 M LiCl or Al(NO$_3$)$_3$. On oxides such as TiO$_2$ and UO$_3$ the selectivity is reversed (Na > Cs).

Several separations of individual alkali metals have been described. A complete separation of the series at tracer level was achieved[61] on zirconium tungstate (mole ratio W:Zr ~ 3:1) dried at 25 ° (Fig. 30), by graded elution, and under similar conditions rubidium and caesium were sharply separated on zirconium phosphate by elution with 1 M and saturated solutions of NH$_4$Cl respectively[62]. Very efficient separations of rubidium and caesium have also been achieved on a macro-scale with zirconium phosphate[63]; after studying the optimum conditions for elution with NH$_4$NO$_3$ as a function of eluant concentration and temperature the separation was carried out at 83°C, 0.1 N NH$_4$NO$_3$ being used to

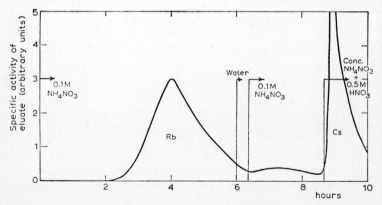

Fig. 31. Separation of caesium and rubidium in macro-amounts on zirconium phosphate[63]. Column 0.36 cm^2 × 2.5 cm, −80 + 120 BSS mesh exchanger. Loading 10%. Flow rate 8–9 ml/h. Temperature 83°C. [Reproduced, with permission, from *J. Inorg. Nucl. Chem.*, 10 (1959) 69.]

elute rubidium and concentrated NH_4NO_3/HNO_3 for caesium (Fig. 31). On columns of length 2.5 cm and diameter 6 mm, with 10% loading and a flowrate of 8–9 ml/h, more than 97% of the rubidium was recovered free from caesium, and more than 99% of caesium free from rubidium. Values of the separation factor α_{Rb}^{Cs}, calculated from these results, lie between 3 and 5 compared with a value of 1.3–1.5 for the organic resin Dowex–50. The data of Kraus and Phillips give values of α_{Rb}^{Cs} equal to $\sim$ 8 in 0.1 M HCl, $\sim$ 4 in 6 M HCl and $\sim$ 2.5 in NH_4Cl. Zirconium tungstate has also been used on very small columns for the rapid separation of tracer quantities of short-lived alkali metal nuclides arising in nuclear fission[64].

Separations of alkali metals from the corresponding alkaline earths are readily carried out on the hydrogen form of zirconium phosphate; thus[23(a)] strontium may be eluted with 0.1 M NH_4NO_3 followed by rubidium with 1 M HNO_3. The ^{137}Ba daughter of ^{137}Cs may similarly be removed from a column on which the former has been absorbed[65] by washing with 1 M HCl. This is a convenient way of obtaining the pure daughter nuclide, which grows in continuously. Good separations between the individual alkaline earths have been reported at tracer level on zirconium molybdate[22(b)], which is also very effective for separation of individual alkali metals (Fig. 32), while zirconium chromate has been used for the determination of ^{90}Sr in sea-water[66].

The reversal of selectivity shown by the hydrous oxides enables group separations involving the rare earths to be achieved; alkaline earths and rare earths may be absorbed together on ZrO_2, followed by elution of the former with 1 M NH_4Cl and the latter with 1 M HCl[59]. Caesium and barium have been separated on UO_3 by elution with 1 M NaOH and 10 M NH_4NO_3, and caesium and europium on ZrO_2 with 0.5 M NH_4NO_3 and 1 M HNO_3[22(b)]. Silica gel has also been used in alkaline solution to remove traces of caesium and strontium[67].

Several separations of transition and heavy metal ions have been described, e.g. that of cobaltous and ferric ions on zirconium tungstate[22(b)], eluting the former with 0.5 M $KNO_3/1$ M HNO_3

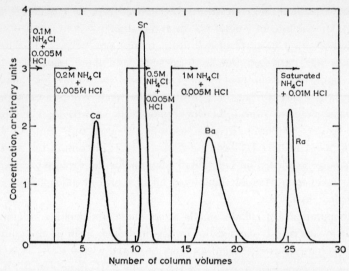

Fig. 32. Separation of the alkaline earths at tracer concentrations on zirconium molybdate[22b]. Column 0.19 cm² × 10.0 cm. Flow-rate 1.1 cm/min. [Reproduced by permission of the United Nations Organisation.]

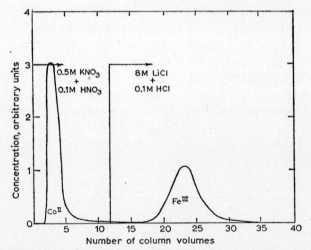

Fig. 33. Separation of cobaltous and ferric ions on zirconium tungstate[22b]. Column 0.09 cm² × 5.5 cm. Flow-rate 0.5 cm/min. [Reproduced by permission of the United Nations Organisation.]

followed by the latter with 8 M LiCl/0.1 M HCl (Fig. 33). Copper(II) and gold(III) have also been separated in HCl solution, and silver(I) and copper(II) from sulphate solution[68]; in both these cases complexing elution was employed.

Separations of uranium, plutonium and fission products have been reported on silica gel[21,69], MnO_2[70], zirconium and titanium phosphates[71]. In the case of MnO_2 99.2% of the fission products remained on the column after eluting uranium and plutonium with 0.1 N HNO_3. Separations on both zirconium and titanium phosphates employed materials prepared by slow precipitation from HCl solutions and pretreated with a solution of phosphoric and hydrochloric acids before use, in order to achieve a high capacity. Several separations are reported between pairs of elements, as well

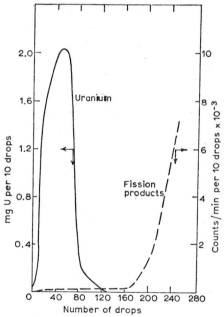

Fig. 34. Separation of uranium and fission products by elution from zirconium phosphate with tributyl phosphate–nitric acid[71]. Column: 0.26 cm^2 × 8.0 cm. Eluant: TBP saturated with 4 N HNO_3. Flow rate: 0.2 cm/min.
[Reproduced by permission of the United Nations Organisation.]

as the elution from a mixed solution of ^{90}Sr, ^{90}Y + ^{144}Ce, UO_2^{++} and ^{137}Cs in that order using 0.1 N HCl, 1 N HCl, 6 N HCl and 5 N NH$_4$Cl respectively. In order to remove uranium (as UO_2^{++} ion) while leaving fission products on the column, elution with tributyl phosphate was employed (Fig. 24).

Effect of Drying Temperature on the Selectivity of Zirconium Phosphate

The selectivity of organic ion exchange resins is known to increase as the degree of cross-linking is increased; consequently, if we assume that the increased condensation which occurs when zirconium phosphate is dried at high temperatures (> 100 °C) is analogous to additional cross-linking, we would expect that increase in the temperature of drying would favour increased selectivity, perhaps at the expense of some loss in capacity. This has been found to hold[72] for zirconium phosphate dried at 260 °C, where the capacity decreased over the pH range 8–11 and increased slightly between pH 2 and 7; this suggests that condensation involves principally the more weakly acid groups, and is in agreement with earlier measurements of the capacity as a function of drying temperature. Distribution coefficients for a number of cations increased to different extents as a result of heating, the order of magnitude of the increase being

$$Tl^+ > K^+ \geqslant Rb^+ \geqslant Cs^+ > Na^+ > Li^+ \quad \text{and} \quad Ba^{++} > Sr^{++}.$$

As a result of this variation the separation coefficients α vary as the drying temperature is changed; in addition, the rates of uptake decrease with increasing drying temperature, particularly for the larger cations. Elution curves and column experiments show that improvements may be effected in the separations of Sr^{++} from Cs^+ and of Li^+ from Na^+ by using material dried at 260 °C. If the drying temperature is too high the uptake is negligible, as shown by the following figures for caesium (0.25 meq in 30 ml 2 N HCl):

Drying temperature, °C	50	260	850
K_d, ml · g^{-1}	7	45	<1

The results of Veselý and Pekárek[32] (Table 25) conflict to some extent with these findings, the distribution coefficients for all cations decreasing when the drying temperature is increased, although it is not possible from these authors' results to ascertain whether the decrease is uniform for all cations or whether varying decreases in individual distribution coefficients lead to increases in separation factors. A uniform decrease would be expected if the only effect of heating were removal of the exchangeable hydrogen atoms on acid phosphate groups, but if in addition the increased cross-linking introduces steric and additional free energy factors, particularly in the absence of swelling, these could lead to differences in equilibrium constants and hence in distribution coefficients. It is likely that the situation is a complex one, and in the absence of more data on the effect of temperature upon the ion-exchange properties it is not possible to reach a firm conclusion.

Paper Chromatography Using Zirconium Phosphate and Similar Materials

As in the case of the heteropolyacid salts (p. 81) the use of exchangers based on oxides and acid salts has been extended to paper chromatography. For this the paper is prepared by soaking in an acid solution of a zirconium salt, after which the precipitating agent (NH_4OH, phosphate, molybdate etc.) is added to produce the exchanger within the paper, which is then washed and dried in air[73,74]. Table 27 shows a number of R_F values in HCl solution, from which it is possible to achieve the following separations:

Co^{II}, Cu^{II}, Fe^{III}
Cr^{III}, Cu^{II}, Fe^{III} } using 0.035 N HCl/0.045 N NaCl
UO_2^{2+}, Fe^{III}, Th^{IV} (or Ti^{IV}) using 2 N HCl/4 N NH_4Cl
Mn^{II} (or Cr^{III}), Al^{III}, Fe^{III} using 0.5 N HCl

Separations of the heavy radioelements may also be achieved[75], *e.g.* AcB/AcC″, ThB/ThC, AcX/Fr; different valency states of the same element may also be separated in many cases[96]. It is interesting to note that the strong affinity of zirconium phosphate

TABLE 27

R_F VALUES ON PAPER IMPREGNATED WITH ZIRCONIUM PHOSPHATE[73]

Element	Developing solution		
	0.1 N HCl	0.5 N HCl	1.0 N HCl
Li	0.82	—	—
Na	0.68	0.77	0.83
K	0.53	—	—
Rb	0.12	—	—
Cs	0	—	—
Ca	0.81	—	—
Sr	0.81	—	—
Ba	0.60	—	—
Ra	0.44	—	—
Co	0.67	—	—
Ni	0.61	0.80	0.85
Zn	0.69	—	—
Cu	0.59	—	—
Cd	0.60	—	—
Hg	0.67	—	—
Fe^{III}	0	0	0.4
Al^{III}	0.13	0.40	0.90
Cr^{III}	0.75	0.80	—
Ce^{III}	0.19	—	—
La^{III}	0.31	0.73	0.80
Ti^{IV}	0	0	0
Th^{IV}	0	0	0
UO$_2$^{VI}	0	—	—

for thallous ion is reversed on the oxide. The alkaline earths may be separated together from caesium by development on zirconium molybdate paper with 0.5 N HCl, after which they may be separated[76] from each other with 0.9 N NH$_4$Cl. Development with 0.1 N HCl has also been used to separate Ag$^+$ and Cu^{++} on zirconium phosphate[68] (R_F(Ag$^+$) $= 0$, R_F(Cu^{++}) $= 0.7$–0.8).

EXCHANGE EQUILIBRIA AND THERMODYNAMICS

Several authors have measured distribution coefficients for various cations and selectivity quotients for a number of cation pairs on zirconium phosphate, and to a lesser extent for various anions on hydrous zirconium oxide, but thermodynamic data can only be derived from such measurements if the system is an ideal one, or if the measurements are made over a wide range of exchanger composition.

Baetslé and Huys[49] studied the distribution at tracer concentrations of the ions Cs^+, Rb^+, Sr^{++} and Eu^{+++} on the hydrogen form of zirconium phosphate, and also of the ions Cs^+ and Sr^{++} from mixed solutions containing either Na^+ or NH_4^+ ions as macroconstituents at concentrations from 0.001 to 0.5 M. Except for the system Sr^{++}/Na^+ all the equilibria involved obeyed the law of mass action, the measured selectivity quotients being given in Table 28. The systems Na^+/H^+, K^+/H^+, Ca^{++}/H^+ and Sr^{++}/H^+ were also studied at macro-concentrations of both cations by batch equilibration with mixed salt solutions, and in view of the correspondence between the values of K_H^{Sr} for tracer and macro-concentrations of strontium it is suggested that both methods lead essentially to the same results. This conclusion is misleading, however, since the same is not true for the other systems, $e.g.$ K_H^{Na} does not equal

TABLE 28

SELECTIVITY QUOTIENTS AT TRACER LEVELS ON ZIRCONIUM PHOSPHATE[49]

System		K_H^M	
		Tracer equilibria	*Macroscopic equilibria*
Cs^+	$\rightarrow H^+$	127	—
Rb^+	$\rightarrow H^+$	50	—
K^+	$\rightarrow H^+$	—	7.0×10^{-2}
Na^+	$\rightarrow H^+$	—	1.0×10^{-2}
Sr^{2+}	$\rightarrow H^+$	1.85×10^{-3}	1.7×10^{-3}
Ca^{2+}	$\rightarrow H^+$	—	2.0×10^{-4}
Eu^{3+}	$\rightarrow H^+$	2.8×10^{-2}	—
Cs^+	$\rightarrow Na^+$	98	—
Sr^{2+}	$\rightarrow Na^+$	(440)	—
Cs^+	$\rightarrow NH_4^+$	3.7	—
Sr^{2+}	$\rightarrow NH_4^+$	28	—

The first ion is the displacing ion; values obtained at macro-concentrations have been extrapolated to zero concentration.

$K_{Cs}{}^{Na}/K_{H}{}^{Cs}$ when appropriate values are selected from the two columns of Table 28; furthermore, the results at macro-concentrations indicate definite variations in the selectivity quotient as the exchanger composition is varied. The authors point out that the results are concentration-dependent and that they will not give true thermodynamic data in the absence of information on activity coefficients, particularly in the solid phase. Later work by Baetslé[77] reports the effect of temperature over the range 5–71 °C on tracer ion equilibria between the ions Cs^+, Rb^+, Ca^{++}, Sr^{++}, Eu^{+++} and Ce^{+++} and the hydrogen form of zirconium phosphate as a function of acidity. The appropriate mass action relationships are observed in all these cases, but while the tracer distribution coefficients decrease with increasing temperature for the alkali metals and less so for the alkaline earths, the reverse relationship is found for the rare earths. Selectivity quotients were calculated from these data and used together with appropriate solution activity coefficients to calculate thermodynamic data, assuming ideal behaviour in the solid phase. The results (Table 29) show that while the enthalpies and entropies for exchange of bivalent and trivalent ions are comparable with the values for highly cross-linked sulphonated polystyrene resins, the excess free energies for exchange of Rb^+ and Cs^+ in acid solution (but not for light alkali metals or in neutral media) are very high in zirconium phosphate. The change

TABLE 29

THERMODYNAMIC DATA FOR EXCHANGE ON H-FORM ZIRCONIUM PHOSPHATE[77]

System	$\Delta G°$, 20° C kcal · mole^{-1}	$\Delta H°$, 5–70° C kcal · mole^{-1}	$\Delta S°$ cal · mole^{-1} · deg^{-1}
$Rb^+ \rightarrow H^+$	−2.28	− 9.56	−24.8
$Cs^+ \rightarrow H^+$	−2.60	−10.01	−25.0
$Ca^{2+} \rightarrow H^+$	1.93	− 0.86	− 9.3
$Sr^{2+} \rightarrow H^+$	1.69	− 1.72	−11.1
$Ce^{3+} \rightarrow H^+$	1.34	+ 1.06	− 0.95
$Eu^{3+} \rightarrow H^+$	1.14	0.65	− 1.67

The first ion is the displacing ion. Activity corrections have been applied in solution, but the solid phase is assumed to be ideal.

in entropy, $\Delta S°$, shows no correlation with the hydrated ionic radius, but increases in magnitude as a linear function of the bare ion radius. On this basis, the exchange is envisaged as occurring between covalently-bound hydrogen and hydrated cations in the interstitial liquid, the affinity being inversely proportional to the degree of hydration; during exchange the polarized hydration shell is displaced and the liberated hydrogen ion hydrated. The net change in entropy equals that due to the replacement of one cation by another plus the entropy difference between the hydrated forms of the two ions involved, and the overall value of $\Delta S°$ is thus less for very large hydrated ions such as Li^+ and Na^+ (where the change in hydration number is great) than it is for K^+, Rb^+ and Cs^+, which are largely unhydrated. The values of $\Delta H°$ are much higher than for sulphonated polystyrene resins, and reflect stronger chemical bonding; the very strong affinity for Rb^+ and Cs^+ may represent specific interactions between undissociated phosphate groups and these ions. The quantitative significance of these results is however obscured by the assumption of ideal behaviour in the solid phase, as the data are strictly applicable only to tracer conditions.

An attempt to derive free energies, heats and entropies of exchange for the cations Li^+, Na^+ and K^+ on the hydrogen form of zirconium phosphate was also made by Larsen and Vissars[33], who used a material prepared by slow precipitation from a solution of $ZrOCl_2$ in HCl; on repeated washing with water the product lost phosphate until the molar ratio of PO_4:Zr was 1.16. Batch equilibration in 0.1005 N HCl solutions of the appropriate alkali metal chloride at temperatures from 1.17 to 44.5 °C was followed by displacement of the cation from the solid with cupric ion for analysis. Selectivity constants were corrected for the solution activity coefficients and values of log K' (p. 25) were plotted against the exchanger composition to obtain the thermodynamic equilibrium constant K by integration beneath the curve, assuming that the results could be linearly extrapolated over the entire composition range. The free energy was obtained from the relationship $\Delta G° = -RT \ln K$ and the entropy change from $\Delta G° = \Delta H° - T \Delta S°$, where the heat of exchange $\Delta H°$ is derived by applying

TABLE 30

$$M^+ + HX \rightleftharpoons H^+ + MX \qquad K = \{\overline{M^+}\}\{H^+\}/\{M^+\}\{\overline{H^+}\}$$

Cation	ΔG° kcal $\cdot$ mole^{-1}	ΔH° kcal $\cdot$ mole^{-1}	ΔS° cal $\cdot$ mole^{-1} $\cdot$ deg^{-1}
Li$^+$	$+2.0$	0.0	-6.7
Na$^+$	$+1.1$	-2.7	-13
K$^+$	$+0.56$	-5.7	-21

Obtained by extrapolation of data measured over a limited range of solid composition.

the Van 't Hoff isochore to the values of K' at the different temperatures. The data obtained (Table 30) express quantitatively the affinity sequence derived from distribution measurements, ΔG° becoming increasingly negative as the hydrated ionic radius decreases; the values of ΔS° are near to the relative entropies of the ions in aqueous solution[78].

TABLE 31

System	K	ΔG° kcal $\cdot$ mole^{-1}	ΔH°, 25–40° C kcal $\cdot$ mole^{-1}	ΔS°, 25° C cal $\cdot$ mole^{-1} $\cdot$ deg^{-1}
Rb$^+$ + CsX $\rightleftharpoons$ Cs$^+$ + RbX	0.56 (20° C)	0.34	—	—
K$^+$ + CsX $\rightleftharpoons$ Cs$^+$ + KX	0.10 (20° C)	1.35	—	—
Rb$^+$ + HX $\rightleftharpoons$ H$^+$ + RbX	1.78 (25° C)	-0.34	-7.6 (mean)	-24.6 (mean)
	1.00 (40° C)	0.00		
Cs$^+$ + HX $\rightleftharpoons$ H$^+$ + CsX	4.83 (25° C)	-0.93	-8.8 (mean)	-26.3 (mean)
	2.36 (40° C)	-0.53		

Solution activity corrections applied and data obtained over the complete range of solid composition.

The significance of these results is obscured by the considerable linear extrapolation which was performed in deriving the equilibrium constant, the maximum loadings being $\sim$ 10%, 30% and 35% for Li^+, Na^+ and K^+ respectively. Only two sets of data have been derived from experiments carried out over the complete range of exchanger composition, the systems being Cs^+/H^+, Rb^+/H^+, Cs^+/Rb^+ and Cs^+/K^+[79,80]. The data were treated by the method outlined earlier (p. 26), with the results shown in Table 31. These investigations show that there is a qualitative difference between the types of isotherm obtained in these systems; whereas the Cs^+/Rb^+ and Cs^+/K^+ exchanges give normal rectilinear isotherms in which exchange favours one ion of the pair over the whole composition range, the Cs^+/H^+ and Rb^+/H^+ systems give an S-shaped isotherm in which the selectivity changes from one favouring Cs^+ (or Rb^+) ion at low uptake to one favouring H^+ ion at high uptake (Fig. 35). This was observed for three different

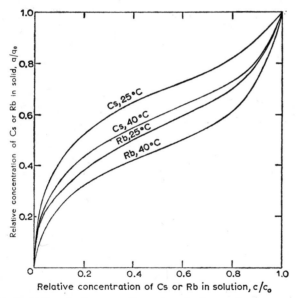

Fig. 35. Rubidium–hydrogen and caesium–hydrogen isotherms on zirconium phosphate[79].

preparations (one of which gave appreciably different values for the thermodynamic data from the other two), and the exchange was found to be reversible, which suggests that this behaviour is due either to heterogeneity of exchange sites (*cf.* Linde Sieve A, p. 57) or to steric factors. It is unlikely that the former is true in view of the shape of the Cs^+/Rb^+ and Cs^+/K^+ isotherms, but the latter is a likely explanation. As a result of the difference in size between Cs^+ and Rb^+ ions on the one hand and of the H^+ ion on the other, progressive replacement of a small cation by a much larger one in an exchanger which cannot swell appreciably will cause exchange to become increasingly more difficult and may ultimately lead to a reversal in selectivity, the free energy of exchange being less negative due to additional contributions from strain free energy. In the case of the systems Cs^+/Rb^+ and Cs^+/K^+ the similarity in size of the cation would lead to normal behaviour, and it would be interesting to extend these measurements to the ower alkali metals.

The data in Table 31 are in general agreement with those of Baetslé (Table 29) and of Larsen and Vissars (Table 30). In particular, the limiting values of log K' at loadings near zero for Cs^+ and Rb^+ on zirconium phosphate agree fairly closely with Baetslé's values for the selectivity constants from tracer solutions (3.6 and 4.8, ref. 79, compared with 3.8 and 4.3, ref. 77); the mean entropies of exchange (-24.6 and -26.3 e.u. for Rb^+ and Cs^+ respectively) correspond to Baetslé's values of -24.8 and -25.0 e.u. and are somewhat greater than the relative entropies of the ions in aqueous solution (-29.7 and -31.8 e.u.), in conformity with the findings of Larsen and Vissars for the lighter alkali metals. Similar detailed examination of other equilibria would be worth while.

KINETICS OF EXCHANGE

The first semi-quantitative measurements of the rates of exchange of ions with granular zirconium phosphate and oxide showed[23(b),26] that rapid initial uptake was followed by a slower absorption, the two stages presumably corresponding to surface exchange and diffusion into the interior respectively. For large ions, appreciable particle sizes, and solution concentrations greater than 10^{-3} N, the rate of exchange decreased with increased particle size and was unaffected by the rate of stirring of the solution, indicating that the rate-controlling step is diffusion of the exchanging ions within the solid. In 10^{-3} N solutions dependence upon both particle size and stirring rate indicated that both particle diffusion and liquid film diffusion are rate controlling. In this respect the behaviour parallels that of organic resins[81].

Nancollas and Paterson have described quantitative measurements upon hydrous thoria and zirconium phosphate[29] using both limited bath and infinite bath techniques. In the former, samples of exchanger were equilibrated with solution and the extent of exchange determined at different times either by direct titration

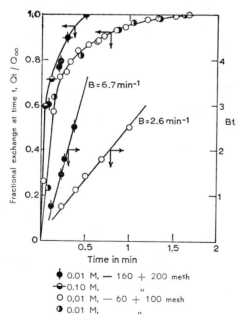

Fig. 36. Kinetics of sodium–hydrogen exchange on zirconium phosphate[29]. [Reproduced, with permission, from *J. Inorg. Nucl. Chem.*, 22 (1961) 259.]

of liberated hydrogen ion or by potentiometric titration; the systems studied were the Na^+/H^+ exchange on zirconium phosphate in acid solution and the Na^+/H^+ exchange on hydrous thoria from alkaline solution. In the infinite bath technique a sample of zirconium phosphate was equilibrated with $5 \cdot 10^{-5}$ M CsCl $+$ 0.1 M KCl, after which the same solution containing tracer ^{137}Cs was passed through the bed for a predetermined time, followed by determination of the caesium uptake by counting. Direct plots of the percentage exchange as a function of time showed a rapid initial uptake followed by a slower exchange (Fig. 36). Under the conditions studied (0.01–1.0 M Na^+, 60–200 mesh BSS exchanger) the rate was independent of sodium ion concentration and unaffected by stirring or shaking speed, but was dependent upon particle size in a manner indicating that particle diffusion is the rate-controlling process. The results were analysed by the theory developed by Boyd et al.[72] for diffusion into spherical particles, which fits the data over a wider range of conversion than does the simple $\sqrt{t}$ plot used by Barrer (p. 66). According to this treatment the fractional exchange F at time t for particles of radius r is given by the expression

$$F = 1 - \frac{6}{\pi^2} \sum_{n=1}^{\infty} \frac{\exp(-n^2Bt)}{n^2} \tag{1}$$

where

$$B = \frac{\pi^2 D^i}{r^2} \tag{2}$$

D^i is the *effective diffusion coefficient* of the two ions undergoing exchange within the exchanger. Values of Bt as a function of F may be derived from eq. (1) and have been tabulated by Reichenberg[83]. If therefore the exchange is particle-diffusion controlled, and if D^i is independent of F, a plot of Bt versus t will be a straight line passing through the origin; its slope will be B, and if the particle radius is known the value of D^i may be calculated. Fig. 36 shows that these conditions hold almost to complete exchange for the systems studied by Nancollas and Paterson, and similar meas-

TABLE 32

EFFECTIVE IONIC DIFFUSION COEFFICIENTS (D^1)
FOR INORGANIC EXCHANGERS

Exchanger	Cation	D^1, cm$^2 \cdot$ sec^{-1}	Reference
		(a) Simple cations	
Zirconium phosphate			
(a) granular (AERE)	Cs$^+$	1.1×10^{-8} (20° C, pH 2.5)	Amphlett and MacDonald, unpublished work.
(b) compacted finely particulate material	Na$^+$	1.0×10^{-6} (25° C, pH 3)	Nancollas and Paterson, ref. 29.
Thorium dioxide, unfired	Na$^+$	4.1×10^{-7} (25° C, pH 13)	idem, ibid.
Sulphonated polystyrene resin			
17% divinyl benzene	Na$^+$	1.15×10^{-6} } (20–25° C)	Reichenberg, *J. Am. Chem. Soc.*, 75 (1953) 589.
5% divinyl benzene		7.3×10^{-6}	
Carboxylic acid resin IRC–50	Na$^+$	3.92×10^{-9} (20–25° C)	Conway, Green and Reichenberg, *Trans. Faraday Soc.*, 50 (1954) 511.
		(b) Quaternary alkylammonium ions	
Zirconium phosphate (glassy)	NMe$_4^+$	1.66×10^{-9} } Ratio 4.7	Amphlett and McDonald, unpublished work.
	NEt$_4^+$	3.54×10^{-10}	
	NBu$_4^+$	8.8×10^{-11}	
Sulphonated phenol–formaldehyde resin	NMe$_4^+$	2.4×10^{-8} } Ratio 4.8	Kressman and Kitchener, *Discussions Faraday Soc.*, 7 (1949) 101.
	NEt$_4^+$	5.0×10^{-9}	

urements on granular exchangers[84] have shown that, although their behaviour is more complex, linear plots of Bt versus t may be obtained up to $\sim 40\%$ conversion, and effective diffusion coefficients may be calculated for them also.

The calculated values of D^1 (Table 32) show that exchange is much more rapid in exchangers of this class than in the aluminosilicates (Table 18), and is in fact intermediate between those in the strongly acid sulphonic resins and the weakly acid carboxylic resins, in harmony with the fact that the acidity of zirconium phosphate is intermediate between those of the two types of resin. The calculation of D^i depends upon measurement of the particle radius, which is difficult for the irregularly-shaped particles of the inorganic exchangers; two methods have been employed, *viz.* direct measurement of a mean radius obtained from microscopic examination of a number of particles, and comparative measurements based on dye absorption. In general the latter method gives better agreement for irregular particles when checked against the slopes of the Bt–t curves for two particle sizes. The values of D^i quoted for the inorganic exchangers are subject to a further reservation in that the exchanger particles are not homogeneous as are the resin beads, but are composed of aggregates or agglomerates of finer particles which are bound together into the bulk solid particles. Diffusion therefore takes place within the channels between the component micro-particles as well as into their interior, and the true micro-particle size will be smaller than the effective particle size of the agglomerate. Consequently, the values of D^i in Table 32 will give an optimistic picture of the rate of diffusion into the solid by comparison with that in organic resins; nevertheless, the practical implication that inorganic ion exchangers of these particle sizes show rates of exchange approaching those of strongly acid cation-exchange resins remains unchanged.

INORGANIC ION EXCHANGERS IN WATER PURIFICATION SYSTEMS

The possibility that inorganic exchangers such as zirconium phosphate and zirconium oxide could be used directly for the removal of ionic impurities from water at the high temperatures characteristic of moderator and coolant circuits in pressurized water reactors ($\sim 300\ °C$) has proved a powerful incentive to their study in many countries. It has been shown[23(a),36] that they possess good physical stability under both static and dynamic conditions and that exchange proceeds efficiently at 300 °C. Reactor water circuits are however normally operated at a neutral or alkaline pH, where the steady loss of phosphate by hydrolysis of zirconium phosphate would be deleterious. Since zirconium oxide readily absorbs phosphate from solutions at all temperatures and at linear flow rates up to at least 11 cm/min, a possible solution would be to use a dual-bed system with columns containing zirconium phosphate and zirconium oxide in that order to remove both cations and anions without releasing significant quantities of phosphate to the circuit. Column tests on the individual exchangers have revealed the following features[36]:

(i) ZrO_2 removes ^{137}Cs inefficiently from an alkaline feed solution (LiOH, pH 10.1) at 25 °C, presumably because of the high ratio of Li^+/Cs^+ ($10^4:1$) and the relatively poor selectivity of the oxide; breakthrough occurred after only 10 column volumes. ^{89}Sr is very effectively removed under the same conditions, no breakthrough being observed after 5000 column volumes for an average removal of 97.8%; ^{60}Co was removed with 97% efficiency at 25 °C and 93.5% at 238 °C.

(ii) Zirconium phosphate removed ^{89}Sr efficiently ($> 99.9\%$) at pH 3.7 and 25 °C even after 5700 column volumes.

(iii) Two columns in series containing zirconium phosphate followed by zirconium oxide were used at 25 °C with a neutral feed solution containing tracer caesium and iodide ions. The influent pH to the second column was reduced to 3 by the acid phosphate ion released from the first, permitting the oxide bed to function efficiently as an anion exchanger. Iodide absorbed by the second column was gradually displaced by phosphate as the latter was absorbed, leading to appreciable leakage of iodide after $\sim$ 2000 column volumes; complete elution of iodide occurred when the oxide had been converted to phosphate, after which the second bed functioned efficiently as a cation exchanger. The phosphate content of the final effluent up to this point was less than 0.1 ppm. These tests have not been repeated at 300 °C and therefore the practical feasibility of such systems is at present uncertain, since single-column tests on zirconium phosphate at 300 °C with alkaline feed solutions show[50] that phosphate is released very rapidly, and the problem of controlling a dual-bed system in which cation and anion exchanger are rapidly changing places would be severe. As the other cation exchangers of this type which have been studied are all less stable towards hydrolysis than zirconium phosphate there seems little point in investigating other combinations. It may be possible to use oxides to remove cations at high pH, although the low selectivity for Cs^+ and Rb^+ (which are present in the fission products) in presence of much larger concentrations of the pH-controlling cation (Li^+ or K^+) is a disadvantage. Clearly much further work is necessary before a final assessment can be made.

INORGANIC EXCHANGE MEMBRANES

The stability of inorganic ion exchangers towards high temperatures and ionizing radiation has naturally prompted investigations into the possibility of incorporating them into permselective membranes which would have considerable advantages over those based on organic exchange resins, *e.g.* in fuel cells employing ion-exchange membranes for transport of hydrogen ions. Inorganic membranes would permit higher temperatures to be used and higher efficiencies attained; in addition, zirconium phosphate is hydrophilic and possesses up to three times as many proton sites as a typical sulphonic acid resin. Dravnieks and Bregman[85] have developed a composite membrane at the Armour Research Foundation, 1″ in diameter and 0.03″ thick, consisting of a compressed wafer of powdered zirconium phosphate and Teflon coated with a mixture of zirconium phosphate and platinum black to which platinum screen electrodes were attached. A current density of $3 \text{ A} \cdot \text{ft}^{-2}$ was obtained at a potential of 0.6 V, but above 100 °C pressurization was necessary to retain the water content of the exchanger.

The ionic conductivity of zirconium phosphate of maximum exchangeable hydrogen content [corresponding to the formula $ZrO(H_2PO_4)_2$] was measured by Hamlen[86], using a powder compact 3 mm thick of diameter 17 mm. Thermogravimetric measurements indicated that one molecule of water was lost at 470 ° and a second at 600 °C by condensation of adjacent $-H_2PO_4$ groups, while below $\sim$ 400 °C approximately 1.6 molecules of non-constitutional water were lost. The resistance of the compact was measured for dried and partially-hydrated material and also for compacts which had been soaked for several days in water. The measured resistance was approximately equal to a calculated value based on the analytical data and the known water content, assuming the current to be carried by H^+ ions and the dissociation constant of the acid phosphate groups in the exchanger to be equal to the second dissociation constant of phosphoric acid (*i.e.* for the equilibrium $H_2PO_4^- \rightleftharpoons HPO_4^{--} + H^+$). The activation energy for conduction fell from $\sim$ 10 to $\sim$ 3 kcal as the material became more hydrated, the latter value being characteristic of conductivity in aqueous solutions; continuous washing led, however, to a decrease in conductivity due to hydrolysis of phosphate. A H_2O_2 fuel cell was constructed using a 1 mm-membrane of 90% zirconium phosphate/10% Teflon compressed at 35,000 lbs./in.^{2}, and gave a polarization curve indicating a membrane resistivity of 6000 Ω-cm. The high resistivity and hydrolysis are major drawbacks to the use of inorganic membranes for this purpose.

An alternative method of preparing heterogeneous membranes, which does not however seem applicable to fuel cells, has been described by Alberti[87]. Zirconium phosphate was precipitated from solution on a mat of glass wool fibres, which was then washed and compressed to 0.5 cm thickness after drying at 50 °C. The perm-selectivities of the membrane towards a number of ions in 0.1 N solution were Li^+ 35%, Na^+ 45%, K^+ 64% and Cs^+ 67%.

REFERENCES

1 E. R. Russel, A. W. Adamson, J. Schubert and G. E. Boyd, *U.S.A.E. Comm.*, Report CN–508 (1943); R. H. Beaton, V. R. Cooper, B. A. Fries, T. J. Chapelle, I. Scheft, R. A. Stoughton and E. H. Turk, CN–633 (1943).
2 G. M. Zhabrova and E. V. Egorov, *Russ. Chem. Rev.*, 30 (1961) 338.
3 J. D. Kurbatov, J. L. Kulp and E. Mack, *J. Am. Chem. Soc.*, 67 (1945)

1923; M. H. KURBATOV, G. B. WOOD AND J. D. KURBATOV, *J. Chem. Phys.*, 19 (1951) 258.

4 A. P. RATNER, Doctorate Thesis, Radium Institute, U.S.S.R. Academy of Sciences, Leningrad, 1948; A. P. RATNER AND Z. N. SIMONYAK, *Sb. Rabot po Radiokhim.*, (1955) 17.

5 S. A. VOZNESENSKII, G. A. SEREDA, P. F. DOLGIKH AND L. I. BASKOV, *Reports of Soviet Scientists to Second International Conf. Peaceful Uses of Atomic Energy*, 4 (1958) 189; Z. KOLAŘÍK AND V. KOUŘÍM, *Collection Czech. Chem. Commun.*, 25 (1960) 1000; 26 (1961) 1052.

6 B. P. NIKOL'SKII, *Zh. Fiz. Khim.*, 5 (1934) 266.

7 L. SACCONI, *Discussions Faraday Soc.*, 7 (1949) 173.

8 W. D. TUCKER *et al.*, *Brookhaven Natl. Lab.*, Report BNL–3746, 1958.

9 D. A. SHISHKOV, *Godishnik Minno-Geol. Inst. Sofiya*, (1960) 213; *C.A.*, 57 (1962) 2831.

10 S. N. TEWARI, *Kolloid-Z.*, 149 (1956) 2, 65.

11 R. S. JOHNSON AND W. C. VOSBURGH, *J. Electrochem. Soc.*, 99 (1952) 317.

12 K. SASAKI, *Mem. Fac. Eng., Nagoya Univ.*, 3 (1951) 81.

13 A. KOZAWA, *J. Electrochem. Soc.*, 106 (1959) 552.

14 P. JORDAN, *Helv. Chim. Acta*, 34 (1951) 699.

15 M. J. POLISSAR, *J. Am. Chem. Soc.*, 58 (1936) 1372.

16 W. BUSER AND P. GRAF, *Helv. Chim. Acta*, 38 (1955) 810.

17 K. H. MAXWELL AND H. R. THIRSK, *J. Chem. Soc.*, (1955) 4054.

18 A. K. COVINGTON, T. CRESSEY, B. G. LEVER AND H. R. THIRSK, *Trans. Faraday Soc.*, 58 (1962) 1975.

19 T. GEREVINI AND R. SOMIGLIANA, *Energia Nucl. (Milan)*, 6 (1959) 339.

20 S. AHRLAND, I. GRENTHE AND B. NORÉN, *Acta Chem. Scand.*, 14 (1960) 1059.

21 S. AHRLAND, I. GRENTHE AND B. NORÉN, *Acta Chem. Scand.*, 14 (1960) 1077.

22 (a) K. A. KRAUS AND H. O. PHILLIPS, *J. Am. Chem. Soc.*, 78 (1956) 249; (b) K. A. KRAUS, H. O. PHILLIPS, T. A. CARLSON AND J. S. JOHNSON, *Proc. Second Int. Conf. Peaceful Uses of Atomic Energy*, United Nations, Geneva, 28 (1958) 3.

23 (a) C. B. AMPHLETT, *ibid.*, p. 17; (b) C. B. AMPHLETT, L. A. McDONALD AND M. J. REDMAN, *J. Inorg. Nucl. Chem.*, 6 (1958) 236.

24 K. A. KRAUS, T. A. CARLSON, D. J. COOMBE, J. S. JOHNSON AND H. O. PHILLIPS, *U.S.A.E. Comm.*, Report ORNL–2004, 1957, p. 208.

25 P. COHEN AND R. AMAVIS, French Patent No. 1,249,429 (1960).

26 C. B. AMPHLETT, L. A. McDONALD AND M. J. REDMAN, *J. Inorg. Nucl. Chem.*, 6 (1958) 220.

27 L. BAETSLÉ AND J. PELSMAEKERS, *J. Inorg. Nucl. Chem.*, 21 (1961) 124.

28 E. M. LARSEN, W. C. FERNELIUS AND L. QUILL, *Ind. Eng. Chem.*, 15 (1949) 512.

29 G. H. NANCOLLAS AND R. PATERSON, *J. Inorg. Nucl. Chem.*, 22 (1961) 259.

30 C. B. AMPHLETT, U.S. Pat. No. 3,056,647 (1962).

31 N. MICHAEL AND D. W. FLETCHER, *Trans. Am. Nucl. Soc.*, 3 (1) (1960), paper 9 (session 3).

32 V. VESELÝ AND V. PEKÁREK, *J. Inorg. Nucl. Chem.*, 25 (1963) 697.

33 E. M. LARSEN AND D. R. VISSARS, *J. Phys. Chem.*, 64 (1960) 1732.

34 G. A. MILLS, U.S. Pat. No. 2,446,547 (1948).

35 M. M. MARISIC, U.S. Pat. No. 2,384,946 (1945).

36 N. MICHAEL, W. D. FLETCHER, D. E. CROUCHER AND M. J. BELL, *Westinghouse Report* CVNA–135 (1961).

37 C. B. AMPHLETT, G. H. NANCOLLAS AND T. WILLIAMS, *Chem. Ind. (London)*, (1959) 292.

38 G. VON HEVESY AND K. KIMURA, *J. Am. Chem. Soc.*, 47 (1925) 2540.

39 E. STEGER AND G. LENKROTH, *Z. Anorg. Allgem. Chem.*, 303 (1960) 169.

40 S. Z. HAIDER, *Anal. Chim. Acta*, 24 (1961) 250.

41 E. M. LARSEN AND A. M. GAMILL, *J. Am. Chem. Soc.*, 72 (1950) 3615; J. S. JOHNSON AND K. A. KRAUS, *J. Am. Chem. Soc.*, 78 (1956) 3937.

42 E. MATIJEVIĆ, K. G. MATHAI AND M. KERKER, *J. Phys. Chem.*, 66 (1962) 1799.

43 G. M. MUHA AND P. A. VAUGHAN, *J. Chem. Phys.*, 33 (1960) 194.

44 A. CLEARFIELD AND P. A. VAUGHAN, *Acta Cryst.*, 9 (1956) 555.

45 G. LUNDGREN, *Rec. Trav. Chim.*, 75 (1956) 585; *Svensk Kem. Tidskr.*, 71 (1959) 200.

46 R. PATERSON, *Thesis*, Glasgow, 1962.

47 W. B. BLUMENTHAL, *The Chemical Behaviour of Zirconium*, Van Nostrand, Princeton, 1958, p. 297.

48 C. B. AMPHLETT AND L. A. MCDONALD, *Proc. Chem. Soc.*, (1962) 276.

49 L. BAETSLÉ AND D. HUYS, *J. Inorg. Nucl. Chem.*, 21 (1961) 133.

50 J. R. GROVER AND B. E. CHIDLEY, *Ind. Chemist*, 39 (1963) 31.

51 C. B. AMPHLETT AND P. J. JONES, unpublished work.

52 W. HERR AND H. J. RIEDEL, *Radiochim. Acta*, 1 (1962) 32.

53 I. GAL AND A. RUVARAC, *Bull. Boris Kidrich Inst. Nuclear Sci.*, 13 (1962) 1.

54 H. KAUTSKY AND H. WESSLAU, *Z. Naturforsch.*, 9b (1954) 569.

55 H. O. PHILLIPS AND K. A. KRAUS, *Oak Ridge Report* ORNL–2983, 1960, p. 50.

56 D. NAUMANN, *Kernenergie*, 3 (1960) 10.

57 H. O. PHILLIPS AND K. A. KRAUS, *U.S.A.E. Comm.* Report ORNL–3320, 1962, p. 81.

58 H. O. PHILLIPS AND K. A. KRAUS, *J. Am. Chem. Soc.*, 84 (1962) 2267.

59 K. A. KRAUS *et al.*, *Oak Ridge Report* ORNL–2159, 1956, p. 41.

60 S. E. BRESLER, YU. D. SINOCHKIN, A. I. EGOROV AND D. A. PERUMOV, *Radiokhimiya*, 1 (1959) 507.

61 K. A. KRAUS, T. A. CARLSON AND J. S. JOHNSON, *Nature*, 177 (1956) 1128.

62 K. A. KRAUS AND H. O. PHILLIPS, *J. Am. Chem. Soc.*, 78 (1956) 694.

63 C. B. AMPHLETT, L. A. MCDONALD, J. S. BURGESS AND J. C. MAYNARD, *J. Inorg. Nucl. Chem.*, 10 (1959) 69.

64 E. A. C. CROUCH, J. A. CORBETT AND H. H. WILLIS, *U.K.A.E.A. Report* AERE–C/R 2325,1957.

65 H. O. PHILLIPS, F. NELSON AND K. A. KRAUS, *Oak Ridge Report* ORNL–2159, 1956, p. 37.

66 YU. D. SINOCHKIN, *Radiokhimiya*, 4 (1962) 198.

67 M. MILONE, G. CETINI AND F. RICCA, *Proc. Second Int. Conf. Peaceful Uses of Atomic Energy*, United Nations, Geneva, 18 (1958) 133.

68 M. J. Nunes da Costa and M. A. S. Jerónimo, *J. Chromatog.*, 5 (1961) 456.

69 D. Cvjeticanin, *JENER Rept.*, No. 57, 1958.

70 D. Cvjeticanin and N. Cvjeticanin, *JENER Rept.*, No. 54, 1958.

71 I. J. Gal and O. S. Gal, *Proc. Second Int. Conf. Peaceful Uses Atomic Energy*, United Nations, Geneva, 28 (1958) 24.

72 G. Alberti and A. Conte, *Atti Accad. Naz. Lincei, Rend. Classe Sci. Fis. Mat. Nat.*, 24 (1959) 782; *J. Chromatog.*, 5 (1961) 244.

73 G. Alberti and G. Grassini, *J. Chromatog.*, 4 (1960) 83.

74 G. Alberti, F. Dobici and G. Grassini, *J. Chromatog.*, 8 (1962) 103.

75 J. P. Adloff, *J. Chromatog.*, 5 (1961) 365.

76 J. M. P. Cabral, *J. Chromatog.*, 4 (1960) 86.

77 L. Baetslé, *J. Inorg. Nucl. Chem.*, 25 (1963) 271.

78 W. M. Latimer, *Oxidation Potentials*, Prentice-Hall, New York, 1952.

79 C. B. Amphlett, P. Eaton, L. A. McDonald and A. J. Miller, *J. Inorg. Nucl. Chem.*, 26 (1964) 297.

80 J. Harkin, G. H. Nancollas and R. Paterson, *J. Inorg. Nucl. Chem.*, 26 (1964) 305.

81 J. A. Kitchener, *Ion-Exchange Resins*, Methuen, London, 1957, chapter IV.

82 G. E. Boyd, A. W. Adamson and L. S. Myers, *J. Am. Chem. Soc.*, 69 (1947) 2836.

83 D. Reichenberg, *J. Am. Chem. Soc.*, 75 (1953) 589.

84 C. B. Amphlett and L. A. McDonald, unpublished work.

85 A. Dravnieks and J. Bregman, *Chem. Eng. News.*, 39 (42) (1961) 40.

86 R. P. Hamlen, *J. Electrochem. Soc.*, 109 (1962) 746.

87 G. Alberti, *Atti Accad. Naz. Lincei, Rend. Classe Sci. Fis. Mat. Nat.*, 31 (1961) 427.

88 P. J. Anderson, *U.K.A.E.A. Reports* M/R 2046 (1956); 2194 (1957); *Trans. Faraday Soc.*, 54 (1957) 130.

89 G. A. Parks and P. L. de Bruyn, *J. Phys. Chem.*, 66 (1962) 967.

90 D. P. Benton and G. A. Horsfall, *J. Chem. Soc.*, (1962) 3899.

91 R. Prasad and A. K. Dey, *J. Phys. Chem.*, 65 (1962) 1272; *J. Sci. Ind. Res. (India)*, B20 (1961) 230; *Kolloid-Z.*, 183 (1962) 71.

92 E. J. Duwell and J. W. Shepard, *J. Phys. Chem.*, 63 (1959) 2044.

93 C. B. Amphlett and J. Kennedy, *Chem. Ind. (London)*, (1958) 1200.

94 G. M. Zhabrova and E. V. Egorov, *Radiokhimiya*, 1 (1959) 538.

95 T. Ito and M. Abe, *Bull. Chem. Soc. Japan*, 34 (1961) 1736.

96 M. N. Sastri and A. P. Rao, *J. Chromatog.*, 9 (1962) 250.

97 A. Clearfield and J. A. Stynes, *J. Inorg. Nucl. Chem.*, 26 (1964) 117.

Index

PRINTED IN THE NETHERLANDS

38765